Table of Cont

Month 1 Checklist

READING

The Alphabet: pages 5-6, 30

For success in reading, your child should be familiar with both capital (uppercase) and lowercase forms of each letter and the order of letters in the alphabet. Two of this month's worksheets labeled *Reading* will help your child recall alphabetical order. You can also help your child recall alphabetical order with these activities:

❑ Complete the worksheets.
❑ Sing alphabet songs with your child.
❑ Using index cards or construction paper, make two sets of alphabet cards, one with uppercase letters and one with lowercase. Challenge your child to arrange each set in alphabetical order. For an extra challenge, give your child four or five letters not beginning at *A* (for example, *L, M, N, O,* and *P*) and have him or her arrange these letters in alphabetical order.

PHONICS & SPELLING

Consonants: pages 7, 10, 13, 16, 21, 24, 27
Rhymes: pages 31-32

Of the 26 letters of the alphabet, 21 are consonants. Good readers associate letters and their sounds without hesitation. The phonics worksheets for this month give your child practice in recognizing the sounds of 14 consonants.

❑ Complete the worksheets.
❑ With your child, look through magazines, catalogs, etc., for pictures of objects whose names begin with the sound associated with a particular consonant. Cut out the pictures and paste them on a large sheet of construction paper. Print the uppercase and lowercase forms of the consonant at the top of the paper. Display the collage on the refrigerator door.
❑ When running errands or taking a walk with your child, look for objects whose names begin with a particular consonant. Challenge your child to memorize at least five of the objects noted and recall them when you get home.

3

HANDWRITING

Letters: pages 8-9, 11-12, 14-15, 17-18, 22-23, 25-26, 28-29

Knowing how to print individual letters is a prerequisite to expressing oneself in writing. The handwriting pages for this month show your child how to form the 14 consonants whose sounds have been introduced. Give your child practice in writing these letters with these activities:

❑ Complete the worksheets.

❑ Have your child write letters in flour that has been sprinkled on a table or countertop. Then smooth the surface and reuse the flour for another practice round. Working outdoors, your child could use sand.

❑ Make a flash card for each consonant presented in the worksheets. Print the uppercase and lowercase forms of the letter on opposite sides. Show one side of a card to your child and have him or her print the other form of the same letter. Flip the card to let your child check the answer.

VOCABULARY & WORD STUDY

Antonyms: pages 19-20

Two of the goals of vocabulary development are improving understanding of what is read and enhancing the ability to express oneself clearly. Learning about antonyms, or opposites, is not only helpful in developing vocabulary but is also fun for your child.

❑ Complete the worksheets.

❑ At odd moments, such as waiting in checkout lines, play this word game with your child. Say a word and ask your child to say its opposite. (More than one opposite may be correct.) Take turns.

❑ Ask your child to listen carefully as you say a sentence that is made false by one word, and identify the word that must be changed. Have your child repeat the sentence, replacing that word with its opposite. For example, you might say, "I feel cold in the sun" and have your child replace the word *cold* with its opposite.

COMPOSITION

Prewriting: pages 33-34

Planning what to write about is part of the writing process. Even though your child may not be ready to write whole sentences and paragraphs, he or she can choose topics and identify personal opinions to be expressed. The composition worksheets for this month encourage your child to identify some personal preferences.

❑ Complete the worksheets.

❑ Ask your child to talk about the pictures he or she draws on the worksheets.

❑ Make sure your child has opportunities to create original pictures in addition to using coloring books. Take time to talk about the situations and ideas shown in the original art.

A to Z at the Zoo

  Connect the dots from A to Z. Color the picture.

Recalling alphabetical order (capital letters)

a to z at the Zoo

  Connect the dots from a to z.
Color the picture.

Recalling alphabetical order (lowercase letters)

Lamb in the Sun

 Say each picture name. If the name has the same beginning sound as **lamb**, draw a line from the picture to the lamb. If the name has the same beginning sound as **sun**, draw a line from the picture to the sun.

 Color the pictures whose names have the same beginning sound as **lamb**.

*Recognizing the initial consonant sounds of **Ss** and **Ll***

Writing L and l

 Trace and write the letters.

 Write **L** or **l** to complete each word.

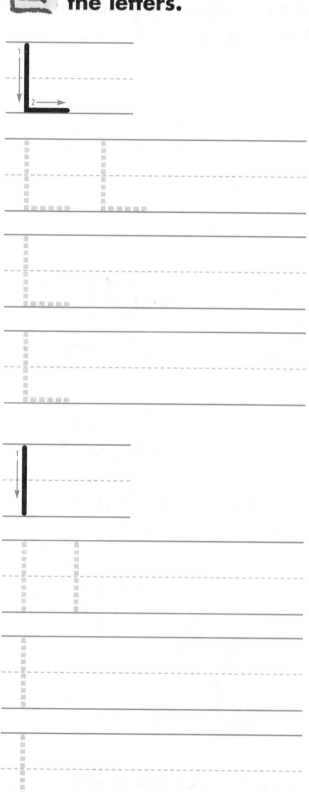

Leo

_eo

_ake

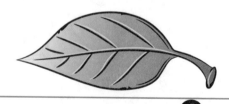

_eaf

Writing S and s

 Trace and write the letters.

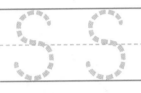

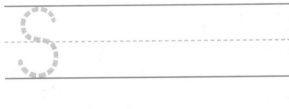

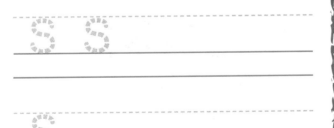

 Write S or s to complete each word.

___am

___oap

___and

Tigers and Monkeys

Say each picture name. If the name has the same beginning sound as **tiger**, draw a line from the picture to the tigers. If the name has the same beginning sound as **monkey**, draw a line from the picture to the monkeys.

Color the pictures whose names have the same beginning sound as **monkey**.

*Recognizing the initial consonant sounds of **Mm** and **Tt***

Writing T and t

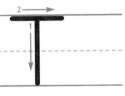 **Trace and write the letters.**

 Write T or t to complete each word.

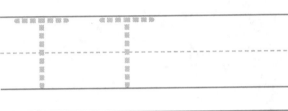

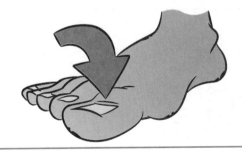

_ina

_oe

10

_en

Writing M and m

 Trace and write the letters.

 Write M or m to complete each word.

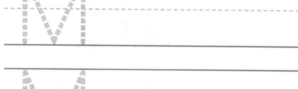

m

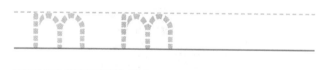

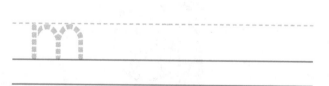

May

_ay

_oon

_ug

Hammer and Nails

 Say each picture name. If the name has the same beginning sound as **hammer**, draw a line from the picture to the hammer. If the name has the same beginning sound as **nail**, draw a line from the picture to the nails.

 Color the pictures whose names have the same beginning sound as hammer.

*Recognizing the initial consonant sounds of **Hh** and **Nn***

13

Writing H and h

Trace and write the letters.

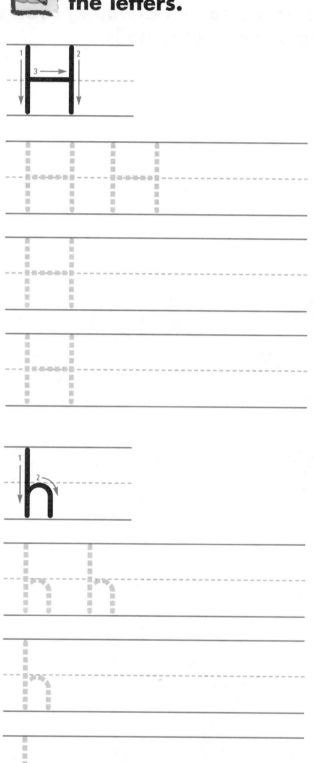

Write H or h to complete each word.

_umpy
Dumpty

_ouse

_i

Writing N and n

 Trace and write the letters.

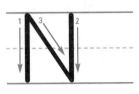

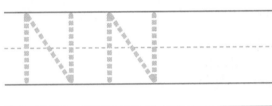

N n

 Write N or n to complete each word.

__ur se

__a __cy

__eck

__u ts

HANDWRITING

A Rose for Bear

 Say each picture name. If the name has the same beginning sound as **rose**, draw a line from the picture to the rose. If the name has the same beginning sound as **bear**, draw a line from the picture to the bear.

 Color the pictures whose names have the same beginning sound as **rose**.

*Recognizing the initial consonant sounds of **Rr** and **Bb***

Writing R and r

 Trace and write the letters.

 Write R or r to complete each word.

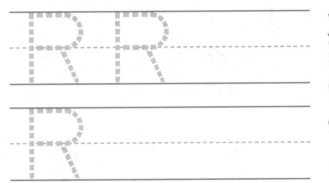

___ o s a

___ a i n

___ o o f

Printing **Rr**

Writing B and b

Trace and write the letters.

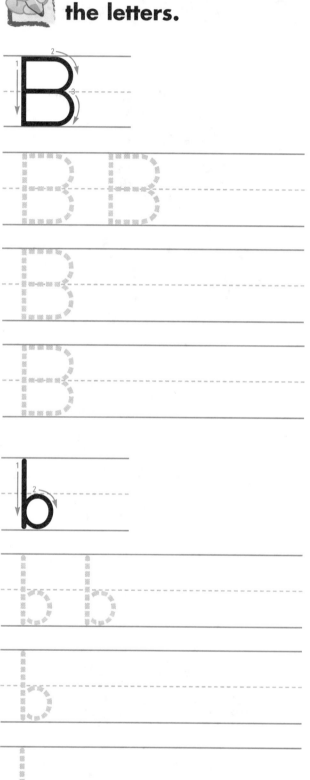

B

BB

B

B

b

bb

b

b

Write B or b to complete each word.

Baby Ben

__ a y __ e n

__ ike

__ a r n

In the Garden

Antonyms are words that have opposite meanings.
Up and **down** are **antonyms**.

up

down

 **Trace the words below.**
Draw lines between the antonyms.

 fast

wet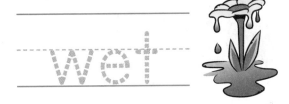

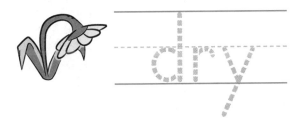 dry

back

 front

slow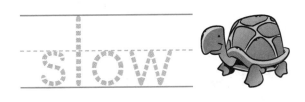

Recognizing antonyms

What's the Opposite?

Antonyms are words that have opposite meanings.
On and **off** are **antonyms**.

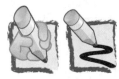 **Trace the words below.
Draw lines between the antonyms.**

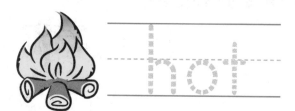 hot   sad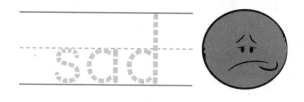

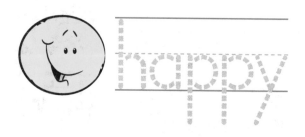 happy   out

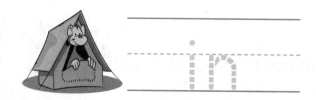 in   cold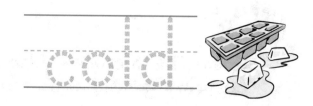

Recognizing antonyms

Violins and Yo-Yos

 Say each picture name. If the name has the same beginning sound as **violin**, draw a line from the picture to the violin. If the name has the same beginning sound as **yo-yo**, draw a line from the picture to the yo-yo.

 Color the pictures whose names have the same beginning sound as **violin**.

Writing V and v

 Trace and write
the letters.

 Write **V** or **v** to
complete each word.

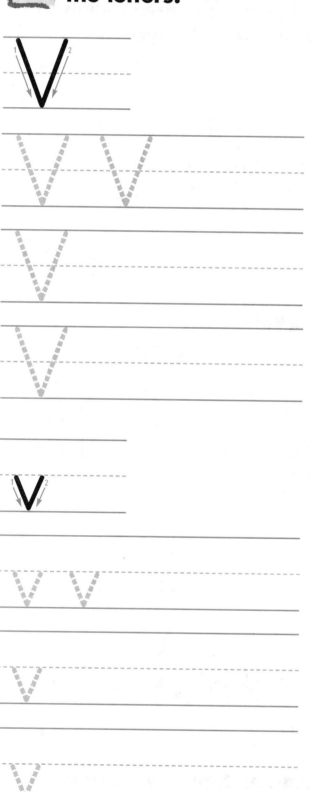

__enus

__an

__ine

Writing Y and y

 Trace and write the letters.

 Write Y or y to complete each word.

____ o a n d a

____ a w n

____ a r d

Printing **Yy**

Pandas around a Fire

 Say each picture name. If the name has the same beginning sound as **panda**, draw a line from the picture to the pandas. If the name has the same beginning sound as **fire**, draw a line from the picture to the fire.

 Color the pictures whose names have the same beginning sound as **fire**.

*Recognizing the initial consonant sounds of **Pp** and **Ff***

Writing F and f

Trace and write the letters.

Write F or f to complete each word.

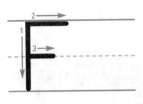

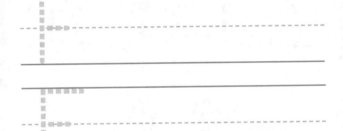

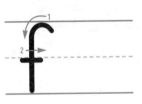

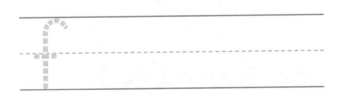

Fred

__ ireman

__ red

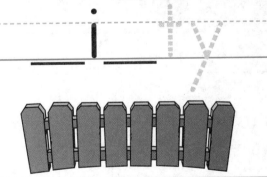
50

__ i __ ty

__ ence

Writing P and p

Trace and write the letters.

Write P or p to complete each word.

__ __ inci __ a __

__ e __ e __ s

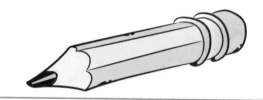

__ enci __

__ o __ co __ n

Printing **Pp**

Cat and Dog

Say each picture name. If the name has the same beginning sound as cat, draw a line from the picture to the cat. If the name has the same beginning sound as dog, draw a line from the picture to the dog.

Dd

Cc

Color the pictures whose names have the same beginning sound as cat.

Recognizing the initial consonant sounds of Cc and Dd

Writing C and c

Trace and write the letters.

Write C or c to complete each word.

C

c c

c

c

c

c c

c

Canada

__anada

__abin

__one

Writing D and d

 Trace and write the letters.

 Write D or d to complete each word.

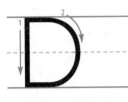

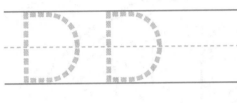

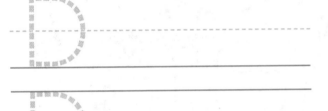

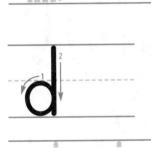

Dr. Dan

___octor

___an

___esk

___aisy

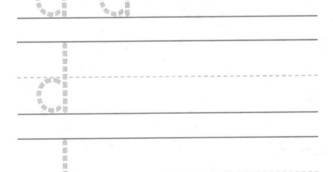

Forest Friends

 Find the 10 hidden letters in the picture below and color them . Use other colors to color the rest of the picture.

Developing visual discrimination

Rhyme Time

Words that rhyme end with the same sounds.
Hug and **bug** rhyme.

 hug

 bug

Trace the words below. Read each word aloud.
Draw lines to match the rhyming words.

Sing for the King!

Sing and **king** have the same ending sounds.
Sing and **king** rhyme.

 **sing**    **king**

Say the name of the first picture in each row. Circle the other pictures in the row whose names rhyme.

*Recognizing words ending with **-en**, **-ig**, **-in**, **-ing**, and **-op***

My Favorite Things

 Color the pet you like best.

 Color the food you like best.

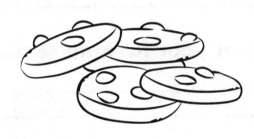

 Color the toy you like best.

Developing self-awareness; evaluating

More of My Favorite Things

 Draw a picture of your favorite place.

 Draw a picture of your favorite season of the year.

Developing self-awareness; evaluating

Month 2 Checklist

Hands-on activities to help your child in school!

READING

Reality and Fantasy: pages 37-38
Sequence and Comprehension: pages 53-54, 65-66

Understanding the sequence of events in an activity or story, distinguishing between reality and fantasy, and using familiar vocabulary to answer written questions are all basic reading skills. Use these activities to help your child develop these skills:

❑ Complete the worksheets.
❑ When watching television shows and videos with your child, take a few minutes to discuss which events are possible, or realistic, and which are impossible, or fantastic. Invite your child to transform a realistic story into a fantasy by replacing one of the realistic happenings with a fantastic one.
❑ Read a favorite comic strip from your local newspaper with your child. Then cut out the strip and divide it into separate panels. Ask your child to reassemble the panels in the correct sequence.

PHONICS & SPELLING

Consonants: pages 41, 44, 47, 50, 52
Rhymes: pages 39-40

Phonics is the study of the sounds of a language. Armed with knowledge of phonics, a child can "sound out" unfamiliar words he or she encounters while reading. The phonics worksheets for this month (*a*) give your child practice in recognizing the sounds of the remaining seven consonants and (*b*) focus on rhyming words—words that share a common ending sound.

❑ Complete the worksheets.
❑ With your child, plan a meal made up of foods whose names begin with a particular letter. For example, for the letter *y*, you might list yams, yogurt, and yellow squash. If you come up with a suitable combination, prepare the meal together.
❑ When selecting books at the library to read to your child, include rhyming books. Encourage your child to guess the word that will finish each rhyme.

HANDWRITING

Letters: pages 42-43, 45-46, 48-49, 51
Use any activities below or from the previous month to give your child practice in writing letters.

❑ Complete the worksheets.
❑ Use tape or magnets to mount a large sheet of shelf paper on the refrigerator. Encourage your child to practice writing on this "chalkboard."
❑ Bake a batch of cookies or cupcakes and have your child decorate each one with a different consonant drawn in frosting.

VOCABULARY & WORD STUDY

Color Words and Other Useful Words: pages 55-61
Antonyms: pages 63-64

The vocabulary sheets for this month introduce some commonly used words that your child will encounter in reading and may need for personal writing. Use the activities below to give your child practice in recognizing both the words on the worksheets and other words that you believe will be useful.

❑ Complete the worksheets.
❑ Make flashcards for all the words introduced on the worksheets. Select five or six and show them to your child one at a time. Praise your child each time he or she reads a word correctly.
❑ Make flashcards of the antonym pairs *fat/thin, full/empty, big/little, new/old, short/long, under/over, wet/dry,* and *left/right.* For example, write *fat* on one side of the card and *thin* on the other. Hold up the cards showing one side at a time. Have your child guess the antonym of the word shown.

Real or Not?

Some stories tell about events that are or could be **real**. We call this kind of story **realistic**.

Other stories tell about events that are make-believe, and do not or could not happen. We call this kind of story a **fantasy**.

 Look at each picture below. If it shows an event that could be **real**, circle **R**. If it shows an event that could not really happen, circle **F** for **fantasy**.

R   F

R   F

R   F

R   F

Discriminating between reality and fantasy

Believe It or Not!

A **realistic** story tells about events that are or could be **real**.
A **fantasy** is a story that tells about events that are
make-believe and could not happen.

 The picture below shows the beginning of a story.
Decide how you want to finish the story and draw
three more pictures to show what happens next. You can
make your story **realistic** or you can make it a **fantasy**.

Which kind of story did you choose to tell?
Circle one.
realistic   fantasy

Discriminating between reality and fantasy

Listening for Rhymes

Tree and **b<u>ee</u>** end with the sound for the letters **ee**.
Tr<u>ee</u> and **b<u>ee</u>** rhyme.

bee   **tree**

 Name the first picture in each row. Color the other pictures
in the row whose names rhyme with the first picture's name.

Silly Rhymes

Words that rhyme end with the same sound or sounds.

 Finish each sentence by writing the word from the box that rhymes with the red word in the sentence.

mail	rug	hat	dog

_____

The **bug** is in the _____ .

_____

I see a **cat** in a _____ .

_____

The **frog** likes the _____ .

_____

The **pail** is full of _____ .

Recognizing words ending in **-ail**, **-at**, **-og**, and **-ug**

A Juggler of Kettles

 Say each picture name. If the name has the same beginning sound as **juggler**, draw a line from the picture to the juggler. If the name has the same beginning sound as **kettle**, draw a line from the picture to the kettle.

Kk

Jj

 Color the pictures whose names have the same beginning sound as **kettle**.

*Recognizing the initial consonant sounds of **Jj** and **Kk***

41

Writing J and j

 Trace and write the letters.

 Write **J** or **j** to complete each word.

_une

_eep

_ewels

Printing **Jj**

Writing K and k

 Trace and write the letters.

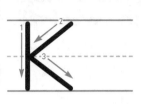

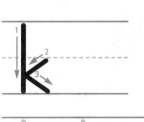

Write K or k to complete each word.

___ing of

Beasts

___ittens

___oala

Printing **Kk**

43

A Garden Windmill

 Say each picture name. If the name has the same beginning sound as **garden**, draw a line from the picture to the garden. If the name has the same beginning sound as **windmill**, draw a line from the picture to the windmill.

 Color the pictures whose names have the same beginning sound as **garden**.

*Recognizing the initial consonant sounds of **Gg** and **Ww***

Writing G and g

 Trace and write the letters.

 Write G or g to complete each word.

G

g

___oodbye

___ai !

___o ld

___a me

Writing W and w

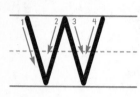 **Trace and write the letters.**

 Write W or w to complete each word.

W

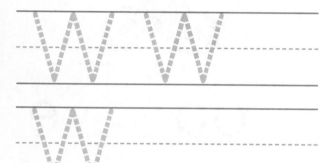

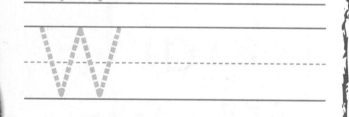

w

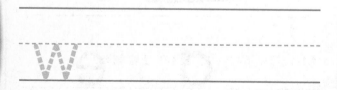

__ e c o m e

__ i l l i e !

__ a r u s

__ o r l d

A Queen and a Zebra

 Say each picture name. If the name has the same beginning sound as **queen**, draw a line from the picture to the queen. If the name has the same beginning sound as **zebra**, draw a line from the picture to the zebra.

 Color the pictures whose names have the same beginning sound as queen.

*Recognizing the initial consonant sounds of **Qq** and **Zz***

Writing Q and q

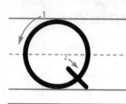

Trace and write the letters.

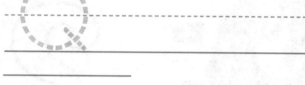

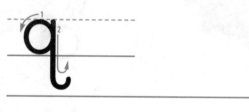

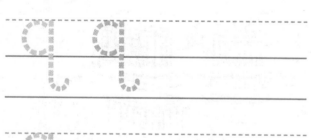

Write Q or q to complete each word.

___uentin

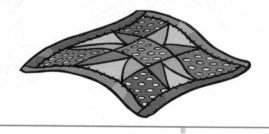

___uilt

___uartet

48

Writing Z and z

 Trace and write the letters.

 Write Z or z to complete each word.

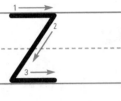

Z

Z Z Z Z

Z Z Z Z

z

z z z z

z z z z

z z z z

Zelda
The Dancing Bear

__e l d a

__i n n i a

__i p p e r

Printing Zz

Two Sounds of x

Name each picture below. Listen for the x sound at the end of each word.

six  **6**

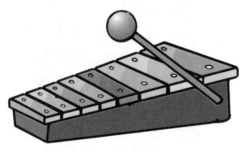 **fox**

The letter **x** makes another sound sometimes. If **x** is at the beginning of a word, it often makes the same sound as **z**.

 **xylophone**

 **Say each picture name.
Draw a line to its correct word.**

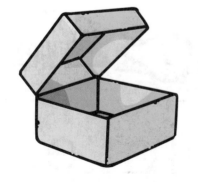

box

ox

ax

tux

Recognizing the two sounds of **x**

Writing X and x

 Trace and write the letters.

 Write X or x to complete each word.

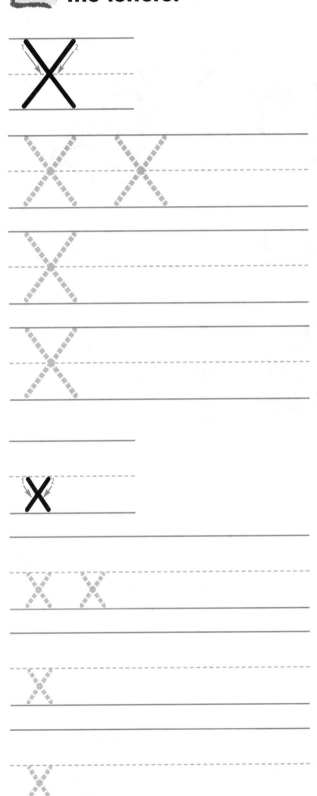

X

X X

X

X

x

x x

x

x

GO XANDER!

__ander

sa__

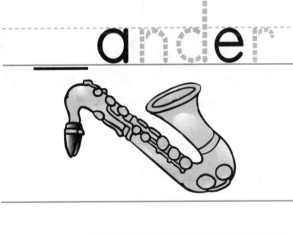

wa__

What's Missing?

Circle the missing letter in each word, then write it to finish the word.

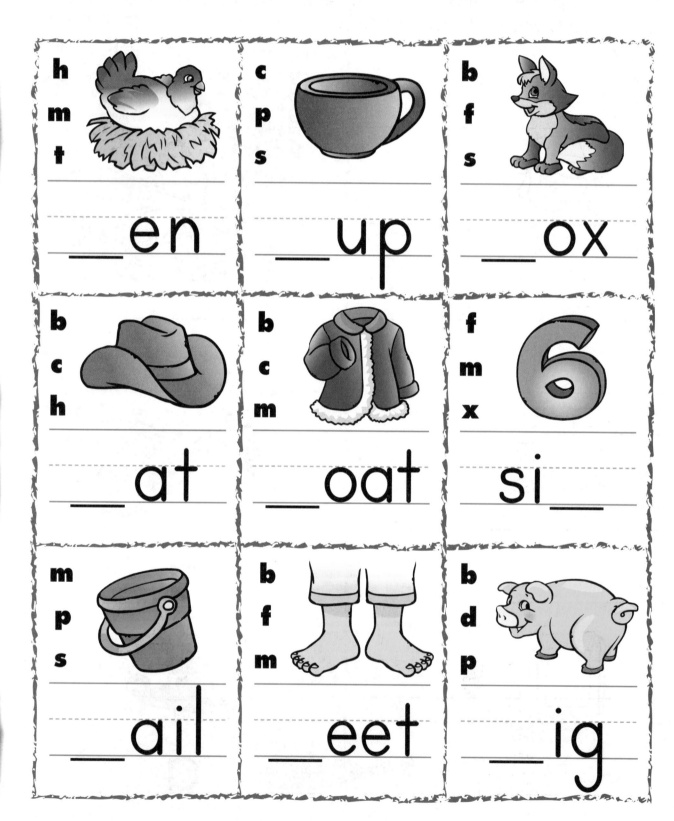

h **m** **t**	**c** **p** **s**	**b** **f** **s**
__en	__up	__ox
b **c** **h**	**b** **c** **m**	**f** **m** **x**
__at	__oat	si__
m **p** **s**	**b** **f** **m**	**b** **d** **p**
__ail	__eet	__ig

Order Please!

 The pictures in each row tell a story. But they are out of order. Write **1** by the event that happened first, **2** by the event that happened next, and **3** by the event that happened last.

Understanding story sequence

Out of Order

 These pictures tell a story, but they are out of order. Number them in order and then tell the story aloud from start to finish.

Understanding story sequence

Under the Sea

Trace the color words. Use the color key to color the picture and find out what is hiding!

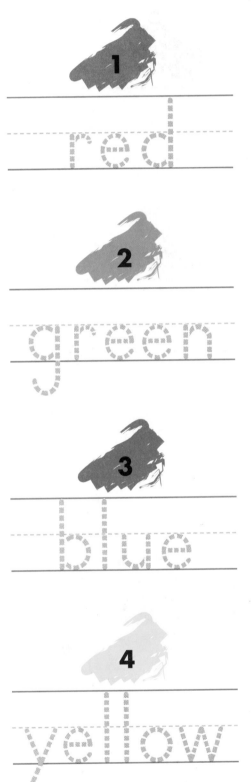

1 red

2 green

3 blue

4 yellow

A Colorful House

Trace the color words.
Use the color key to color the picture.

1
orange

2
brown

3
black

4
purple

Recognizing and writing color words: **orange**, **brown**, **black**, *and* **purple**

Words to Know—People

 Look at each picture and sound out its word.

girl   **boy**   **mother**   **father**

 Draw a line to match each word with its picture.

mother

father

boy

girl

Words to Know—Animals

 Look at each picture and sound out its word.

cat   **dog**   **fish**   **bird**

 Draw a line to match each word with its picture.

dog

fish

cat

bird

*Recognizing commonly used nouns: animals (**cat**, **dog**, **fish**, and **bird**)*

Words to Know—School Tools

 Look at each picture and sound out its word.

pencil   **paper**   **crayon**   **scissors**

Draw a line to match each word with its picture.

crayon

scissors

paper

pencil

Words to Know—Direction

 Look at each picture and sound out its word.

cut　　**color**　　**write**　　**draw**

1. Cut along the ⟋ in Box 1.
2. Color the bird in Box 2.
3. Write **OK** in Box 3.
4. Draw a 🌼 in Box 4.

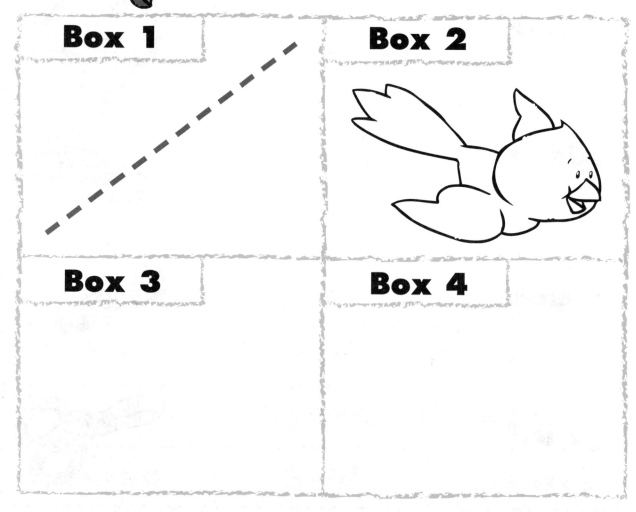

Box 1　　　**Box 2**

Box 3　　　**Box 4**

*Recognizing verbs commonly used in school activities: (**cut**, **color**, **write**, and **draw**)*

What Goes Together?

 Cut out the word slips at the bottom of the page. Paste each word slip onto its correct house.

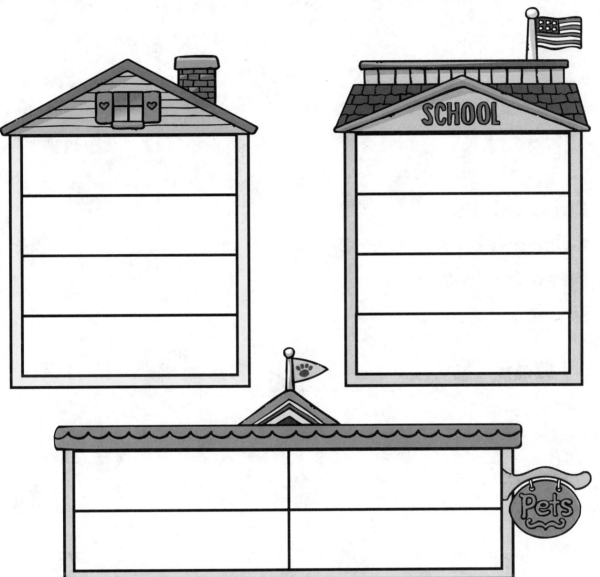

girl	dog	mother
fish	boy	cat
crayon	paper	scissors
father	bird	pencil

Reviewing commonly used nouns; classifying

Antonym Action

Antonyms are words with opposite meanings.
New and **old** are antonyms.

new   old

 Match each word with its antonym.

 **full**

 **fat**

big

thin

little

empty

 Write the antonym for each word.
Use the words in the box to help you.

thin	full	old	big

_____   _____

fat _____   **empty** _____

little _____   **new** _____

Recognizing and writing antonyms

Antonyms Again

Antonyms are words with opposite meanings.

 Match each word with its antonym.

 **short**

 **dry**

 **under**

right

 wet

long

left

over

 Write the antonym for each word.
Use the words in the box to help you.

short	left	under	wet

long _____

right _____

over _____

dry _____

Recognizing and writing antonym

A Beautiful Day

 Look at the picture below.

 Circle the answers.

1. What is in the ?   **bird**   **cat**

2. Who is on the ?   **father**   **girl**

3. What color is the ?   **red**   **purple**

4. Who is on the ?   **boy**   **mother**

Choosing short answers to questions

A Day at School

 Look at the picture below.

 Use the words in the box to help you write the answers.

color	cut	fish	write

1. What will the boy do with the crayon? _____

2. What will the girl do with the scissors? _____

3. What will the boy do with the pencil? _____

4. What did the girl draw on the paper? _____

Writing short answers to questions

Month 3 Checklist

Hands-on activities to help your child in school!

PHONICS & SPELLING

Vowels: pages 69, 71-73, 75-76, 78, 80-82, 84-85, 87, 89-92

While typical consonants are associated with only one sound, the vowels *a, e, i, o* and *u* are associated with more than one sound. Phonics worksheets for this month focus on the short vowel sounds, such as the sounds of short *a* in *rat*, short *e* in *bed*, short *i* in *pit*, short *o* in *hop*, and short *u* in *bug*. Help your child recognize the short vowel sounds with these activities:

❑ Complete the worksheets.

❑ Tell your child to listen for a particular short vowel sound and to clap when he or she hears it. Then say three words, only one of which has that sound. If your child has difficulty choosing the right word, identify the answer and have your child say the word with you, emphasizing the vowel sound. Then repeat the activity with a new set of words.

❑ Have your child make a set of vowel flash cards, printing a different vowel on each card. Then say a series of one-syllable words with short vowel sounds (such as *stand, send, top, sit,* and *run*). Ask your child to hold up the flash card for the vowel sound that is heard in each word.

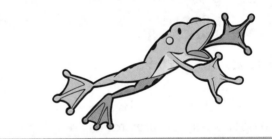

HANDWRITING

Letters: pages 70, 74, 79, 83, 88

This month's worksheets complete the review of all the letters of the alphabet.

❑ Complete the worksheets.

❑ On smooth pavement or sidewalk, have your child write letters with chalk.

❑ Combine handwriting practice with a review of beginning consonant sounds and short vowel sounds. Say a word and have your child write the consonant heard at the beginning of the word. If the word has a short vowel sound, ask your child also to write that vowel.

READING

Comprehension: pages 77, 86, 93-94

Reading is more than simple decoding. The goal of reading is to understand the writer's message. The reading worksheets for this month explore your child's understanding of phrases and sentences in enjoyable puzzles and a familiar story.

❏ Complete the worksheets.
❏ As you read a new story to your child, leave out a word in a sentence and ask your child to suggest an appropriate word to complete the idea. Encourage him or her to use both the words you have read and picture clues to determine what word is needed.
❏ Find crossword puzzles made for children and work them with your child.

COMPOSITION

Prewriting: pages 95-96

One of the ways the writing ability of older children is evaluated is by having the student respond to a writing prompt. The composition worksheets for this month provide prompts to which your child will respond with pictures rather than words. Use these activities to help your child focus on what is expected in a response to such a writing situation and to come up with a personal slant.

❏ Complete the worksheets.
❏ Before reading a story to your child, read only the title and invite your child to guess what the story may be about.
❏ Invite your child to respond to prompts such as these, either verbally or in pictures: things that make me happy, things that make me sad, things that scare me, things that make me laugh. Put the written pages or pictures together to form booklets that the child can read independently.

Hearing the Short a Sound

The words c**a**t and h**a**m have the short **a** sound.

c**a**t  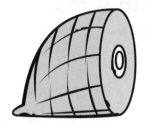 h**a**m

 Say the names of the two pictures in each box. Circle and color the picture whose name has the short **a** sound.

Recognizing the short sound of **a**

Writing A and a

 Trace and write the letters.

 Write A or a to complete each word.

United States of America

U S __

m __ sk

h __ ppy

Apple Has a Short a

Apple and **b<u>a</u>t** have the short **a** sound.

 <u>a</u>pple   b<u>a</u>t

 Say the name of each picture below. If you hear the short **a** sound, write **a** to finish the word.

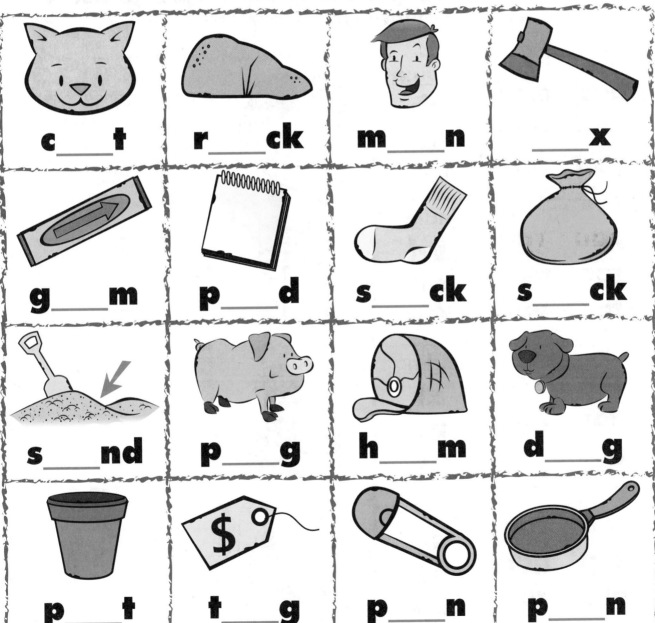

c__t	r__ck	m__n	__x
g__m	p__d	s__ck	s__ck
s__nd	p__g	h__m	d__g
p__t	t__g	p__n	p__n

Meet Some Short a Families

The words **tag** and **bag** end with the sounds for the letters **ag**. **Tag** and **bag** rhyme.

tag　　　　　　　　　　　　**bag**

 Read the rhyming words in each box and circle the ending they share. Use the picture clue to write one more rhyming word.

bad mad	**ending**		
dad pad	**ab**		_____
had lad	**ad**		------
	ag		_____

pan ran	**ending**		
tan man	**ad**		_____
fan van	**an**		------
	ax		_____

pat rat	**ending**		
fat mat	**at**		_____
sat cat	**ar**		------
	ag		_____

lap rap	**ending**		
tap gap	**ab**		_____
nap cap	**at**		------
	ap		_____

*Recognizing word families involving short **a***

Hearing the Short e Sound

The words **r_e_d** and **b_e_d** have the short e sound.

red  bed

 Say the names of the two pictures in each box. Circle and color the picture whose name has the short e sound.

Writing E and e

Trace and write the letters.

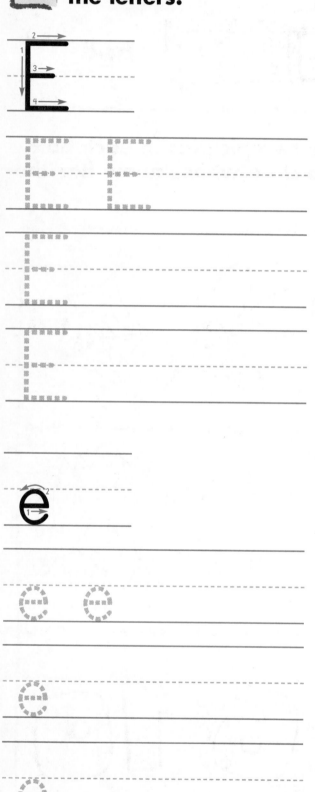

Write E or e to complete each word.

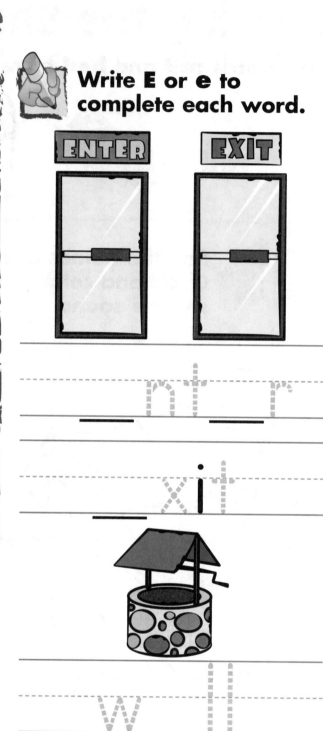

n_t_r

_xit

w_ll

b_nch

Egg Has a Short e

Egg and **b<u>e</u>ll** have the short e sound.

<u>e</u>gg

b<u>e</u>ll

 Say the name of each picture below. If you hear the short e sound, write **e** to finish the word.

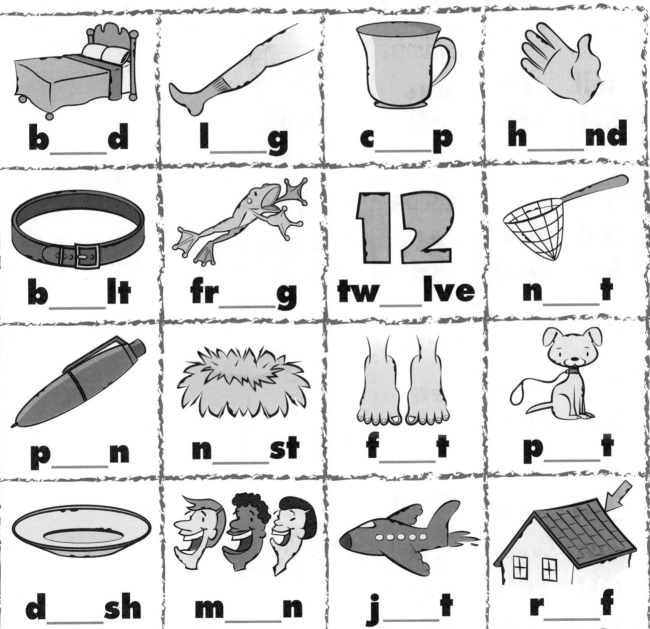

b____d	l____g	c____p	h____nd
b____lt	fr____g	tw____lve	n____t
p____n	n____st	f____t	p____t
d____sh	m____n	j____t	r____f

Meet Some Short e Families

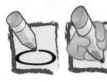

Read the rhyming words in each box and circle the ending they share. Use the picture clue to write one more rhyming word.

bet pet met wet set let	ending el **et** ed	
fell tell bell sell	ending ess **ell**	
red fed led wed	ending et **ed**	
ten den pen men	ending **en** et	
best pest rest west test vest	ending **est** elt ent	

*Recognizing word families involving short **e***

Puzzle Fun

 Use the picture clues and the word clues to finish the puzzle.

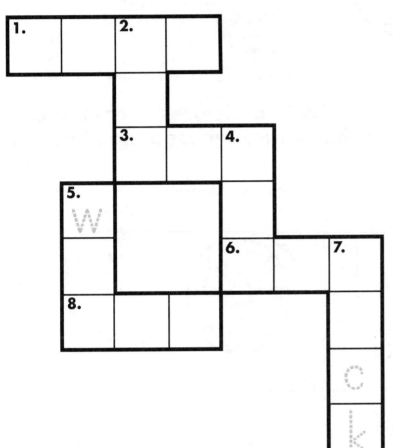

ACROSS

1. Opposite of **boy**

3. This man

6. To write, we use a  or a ____.

8. Opposite of **girl**

DOWN

2. This color

4. This cat can ___.

5. The spins a ___.

7. A has a long ___.

Hearing the Short i Sound

The words **f<u>i</u>sh** and **b<u>i</u>b** have the short **i** sound.

f<u>i</u>sh  **b<u>i</u>b**

 Say the names of the two pictures in each box. Circle and color the picture whose name has the short **i** sound.

*Recognizing the short sound of **i***

Writing I and i

 Trace and write the letters.

I

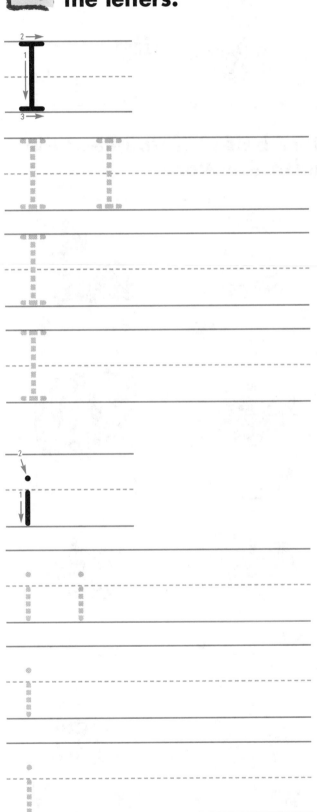

i

 Write I or i to complete each word.

___ona

__guana

k__tchen

m__x__ng

Hill Has a Short i

The words h<u>i</u>ll and d<u>i</u>g have the short i sound.

h<u>i</u>ll   d<u>i</u>g

 Say the name of each picture below. If you hear the short i sound, write i to finish the word.

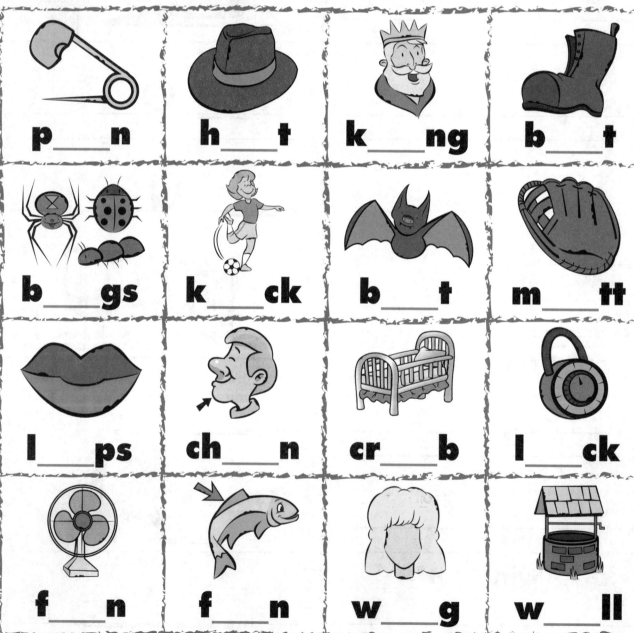

p___n   h___t   k___ng   b___t

b___gs   k___ck   b___t   m___tt

l___ps   ch___n   cr___b   l___ck

f___n   f___n   w___g   w___ll

Completing words with short i

Meet Some Short i Families

Read the rhyming words in each box and circle the ending they share. Use the picture clue to write one more rhyming word.

big dig fig jig rig wig	ending **it** **in** **ig**	_____ _____ _____
lip zip sip dip tip rip	ending **in** **ir** **ip**	_____ _____ _____
hid bid kid rid	ending **ip** **id**	_____ _____ _____
lit hit fit bit quit kit	ending **is** **it** **ig**	_____ _____ _____
fin tin kin win	ending **it** **in**	_____ _____ _____

*Recognizing word families involving short **i***

Hearing the Short o Sound

The words mop and hog have the short o sound.

mop

hog

 Say the names of the two pictures in each box. Circle and color the picture whose name has the short o sound.

Recognizing the short sound of o

Writing O and o

 Trace and write the letters.

 Write O or o to complete each word.

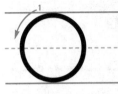

O

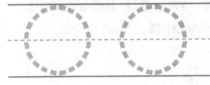

O

O

___ scar

___ tter

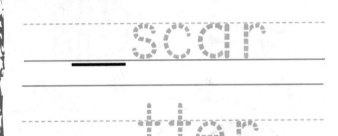

STOP

o

o   o

st ___ p

o

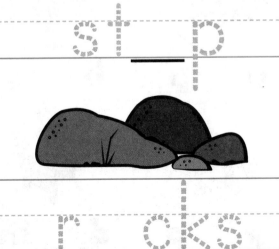

o

r ___ cks

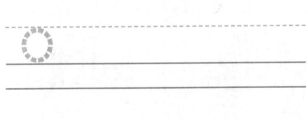

Ox Has a Short o

The words <u>o</u>x and s<u>o</u>ck have the short o sound.

<u>o</u>x   s<u>o</u>ck

 Say the name of each picture below. If you hear the short o sound, write o to finish the word.

p___g   b___x   m___p   h___ll

cl___ck   s___b   s___b   d___ck

p___p   b___g   c___t   c___t

p___p   d___sk   d___ll   r___ck

Completing words with short o

Meet Some Short o Families

 Read the rhyming words in each box and circle the ending they share. Use the picture clue to write one more rhyming word.

		ending		
bob	mob	**ob**		
job	rob	**op**		

		ending		
hop	mop	**od**		
pop	sop	**op**		

		ending		
lot	got	**on**		
rot	not	**og**		
pot	hot	**ot**		

		ending		
dock	sock	**ock**		
flock	rock	**ogs**		

		ending		
dog	jog	**og**		
fog	hog	**op**		

Recognizing word families involving short o

Puzzle Time

 Use the picture clues and the word clues to finish the puzzle.

ACROSS

2. To stop.
   Rhymes with **it**.

4. If he is bad,
   he is ____ good.

6.

7. A ⏰ goes tick-____.

9. The 🏈 will
   ____ the 🏈.

DOWN

1. Part of a fish.
   Rhymes with **pin**.

2. Fast. Rhymes with sick.

3. This toy.

5. This 🥫 is made of ____.

8. Boys and girls are ____.

Applying reading skills to a puzzle

Hearing the Short u Sound

The words d<u>u</u>ck and m<u>u</u>g have the short u sound.

d<u>u</u>ck   **m<u>u</u>g**

 Say the names of the two pictures in each box. Circle and color the picture whose name has the short **u** sound.

*Recognizing the short sound of **u***

Writing U and u

 Trace and write the letters.

 Write U or u to complete each word.

____ ncle

Sam

r__nner

____mpire

Up Has a Short u

The words <u>**up**</u> and **b<u>u</u>g** have the short **u** sound.

 **up**    **b<u>u</u>g**

Say the name of each picture below. If you hear the short **u** sound, write **u** to finish the word.

gl__ss   d__ck   c__b   c__b

r__t   r__g   c__p   c__p

j__t   g__m   c__t   c__t

s__b   f__t   th__mb   c__ff

Meet Some Short u Families

  Read the rhyming words in each box and circle the ending they share. Use the picture clue to write one more rhyming word.

		ending		
rug	tug	**ub**		
hug	dug	**ug**		
bug	mug	**up**		

		ending		
cub	sub	**ub**		
rub	hub	**ud**		

		ending		
fun	run	**un**		
bun	pun	**ug**		

	ending		
sum	**um**		
bum	**un**		
hum			

	ending		
hut	**ut**	
but	**ud**	
cut		

*Recognizing word families involving short **u***

Short Vowel Art

 Read the word in each space and listen for its vowel sound. Use the color key to color in the spaces and reveal the vowel letter being used.

 short **a**

 short **i**

 short **u**

 short **e**

 short **o**

☆

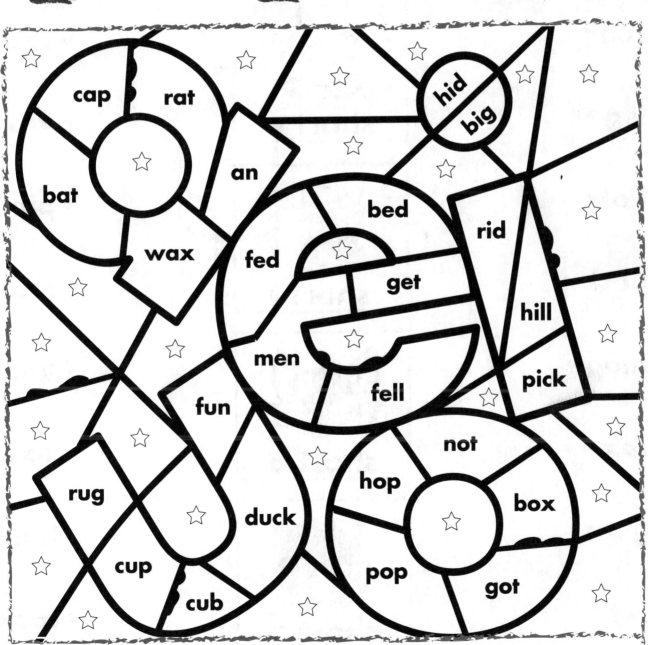

*Reviewing the short sounds of vowels **a**, **e**, **i**, **o** and **u***

Short Vowel Match

 Match each word to the vowel sound it uses.

tan •

will •

run •

leg •

hot •

pack •

mop •

fox •

gum •

set •

short a

short e

short i

short o

short u

• fit

• pup

• sad

• yes

• pin

• mud

• tag

• six

• bet

• rock

*Reviewing the short sounds of vowels **a**, **e**, **i**, **o** and **u***

PHONICS & SPELLING

Goldilocks and the Three Bears

  Fill in the missing words in the story and then read it aloud.

Who the story is about:

Mother Bear  **Goldilocks**

 Father Bear **Baby Bear**

Part 1

The _____ (had, hid) a little

 _____ (in, on) the woods.

One day _____ (Mother, mixer) Bear

said, "I will _____ (fax, fix) a for you."

But the was too _____ (hit, hot). So the

 _____ (went, want) for a walk.

A little _____ (green, girl) named Goldilocks

was _____ (last, lost) in the woods. Goldilocks

saw the and went _____ (in, on).

Turn to the next page to finish the story!

Goldilocks and the Three Bears Part 2

Goldilocks _____ (sat, sot) in Baby Bear's ⛑. She was too _____ (bag, big) for the ⛑ and _____ (at, it) broke.

Goldilocks saw the 🥣 that was _____ (sat, set) out to cool. She ate _____ (all, ill) of Baby Bear's 🥣 ! Then she laid _____ (down, duck) on Baby Bear's _____ (bad, bed).

The 🐻🐻🐻 came _____ (back, buck). They saw the ⛑ and the 🥣. Baby Bear was _____ (sad, sod). His _____ (dad, did) was _____ (mud, mad).

Then the 🐻🐻🐻 saw Goldilocks _____ (and, end) she saw them. Goldilocks jumped _____ (up, us) and ran away— _____ (fast, fist)!

The _____ (End, And)!

Reading a story and supplying missing words

All About Me!

by _____

This is a picture of **ME!**

My best days are when I get to do this. . .

THE END!

4

When I am sick, I do this...

I am sad.

When I am well, I do this...

I am happy.

Month 4 Checklist

Hands-on activities to help your child in school!

PHONICS & SPELLING

Single Consonants: pages 99-102
Consonant Blends: pages 107-113
Long Vowels: pages 117-120, 123-125

Several consonants are associated with more than one sound. The worksheets for this month review the hard and soft sounds of the letters *c* and *g*, as well as the sounds of consonants appearing at the ends of words. This month also introduces consonant blends: combinations of two or three consonants in which every consonant is heard. Initial blends with *l*, *r*, or *s* are developed. Finally, the long sounds of vowels are introduced, beginning with long *a* and long *e*.

❑ Complete the worksheets.

❑ Give your child practice with the different sounds of *c* and *g* as you read stories to him or her. Point out words that begin with *c* or *g*, read each word, and have your child decide whether the beginning sound is hard or soft.

❑ Help your child make a consonant blends scrapbook. Set aside a page for each blend as it is introduced on the worksheets. Have your child search through magazines and ads for pictures of objects whose names begin with any of the blends. Then have your child cut out the pictures and paste them on the appropriate pages.

❑ To help your child become familiar with the different spelling patterns of long vowels, make a long vowel file. For this, you will need an index card file box, a set of 3" x 5" index cards, and divider cards with tabs. On each tab, write a different spelling pattern, such as *a__e*, *ai*, and *ay*. Have your child write a different word on each card and file it behind the correct divider card. Words chosen should be important or difficult for your child. Make adding cards to the file box an ongoing process, and review the old cards after every few days.

COMPOSITION

Rhymes: pages 103-104, 121-122
Completing Sentences: pages 127-128

Creative, original thinking is at the heart of composition. The composition activities for this month provide opportunities for your child to choose words to create sentences and rhymes of his or her choice.

❏ Complete the worksheets.
❏ After reading a rhyme or simple poem to your child, encourage your child to come up with a new final line that completes the rhyme in a different way.
❏ Encourage your child's ability to express him- or herself verbally. For example, at the dinner table, ask him or her to tell what happened during the day, to describe what he or she has seen at school or on television, and to state personal opinions.

READING

Sequence: pages 105-106
Comprehension: pages 114-116, 126

Your child shows understanding of sequence when he or she can place events in time order and figure out which events logically come before or after other events. Another skill developed in this month's reading worksheets is understanding, or comprehension, of short passages. For example, answering a riddle or supplying a word missing from a sentence indicates that a child understands the riddle or sentence.

❏ Complete the worksheets.
❏ Give your child practice in sequential thinking. Each evening, remind your child of one event that happened during the day and have him or her recall an event that happened before it and another event that happened after it.
❏ To develop skills in sequence, when you finish reading a story, ask your child to retell some part of it in his or her own words. As needed, help your child identify the order of the events.
❏ Get simple riddle books from the library or bookstore. Each day read a few riddles to your child, and challenge him or her to come up with the answers independently.

Hard g and Soft g

Hard g
If g comes before the letters **a**, **o**, or **u** it has a hard sound like **gum**.

Soft g
If g comes before the letters **e**, **i**, or **y** it often has a soft sound like **j**.

goose   **gave**   **gum**

general   **gypsy**
gingerbread

The **g** does not always have the soft sound before **e** or **i**. Sometimes it has the hard sound, like in **girl**, **get**, and **give**.

 Say the words below aloud. Circle each **g** and the letter after it. Color the pictures whose names have the soft sound of **g**.

giraffe

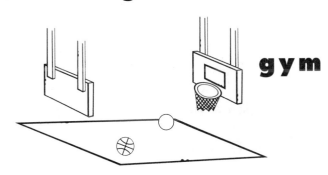 **gym**

gems

 **gold**

The Two Sounds of c

Hard c
If **c** comes before **a**, **o**, or **u** it has the hard sound like **k**.

<u>c</u>at   <u>c</u>ub   <u>c</u>ot

Soft c
If **c** comes before **e**, **i**, or **y** it has the soft sound like **s**.

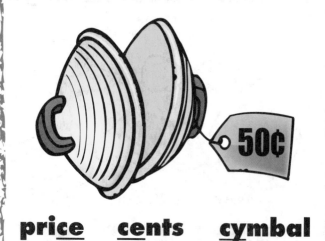

pri<u>c</u>e   <u>c</u>ents   <u>c</u>ymbal

 Say each word aloud. If you hear hard **c**, draw a ◯ around it; if you hear soft **c**, draw a ☐.

celery

car

colors

cone

mice

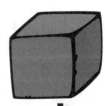

cube

fence

comb

lace

*Recognizing the hard and soft consonant sounds of **c***

Hearing Endings

Say the picture name.
Fill in the ◯ next to the correct word.

◯ map   ◯ man

◯ bun   ◯ bud

◯ fan   ◯ fat

◯ bell   ◯ bet

◯ ham   ◯ hat

◯ miss   ◯ mitt

◯ win   ◯ wig

◯ cub   ◯ cup

◯ cot   ◯ cob

◯ hen   ◯ hem

◯ bob   ◯ box

◯ wet   ◯ web

Recognizing the sounds of consonants in final position

Animal Tales

 **Read each sentence in the story. What letters are missing? Write the missing letters.**

I am Spot, a **do** ____.

I am Ann's **pe** ____.

My fur is black and **ta** ____.

If I like someone, I **wa** ____ my tail.

I am Pip, a **ca** ____.

I like to take a **na** ____.

I like to nap on a **be** ____.

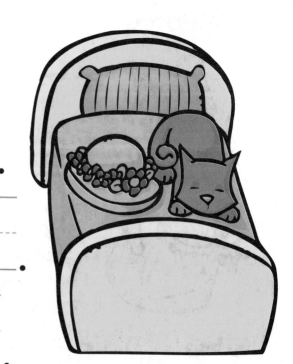

I nap next to a **ha** ____.

Rhyme It Your Way

 Write a letter from the box in each blank space to make your own rhyme. Then draw a picture about your rhyme.

d f h j m p t w

Rhyme

Picture

If you come and dig _____

you will find a _____ ig.

Can you hop _____

over my _____ op ?

I have a friend named Ben. _____

He gave me his old _____ en.

Who Had a Pet Bug?

 Use the letters in the box to write three rhyming words for each word shown below.

b	d	g	h	l	m	p	s	t	w

had

pet

bug

 Choose one set of the rhyming words to write your own rhyme.

Writing original rhymes based on given words

A Walk in the Woods

 Read the story.

Dan was taking a walk. First he saw a bird.
Then he saw a deer. Next he saw a rabbit.
Then Dan saw a skunk, and he ran away!

 The pictures below show the **events** in the story. **Events** are the things that happened in the story. Number the **events** in the order they happened from 1 to 4.

Understanding story sequence

A Surprise Box

 Read each sentence and draw a line to its matching picture. Then number the events in order from 1 to 4. Write the numbers in the ☐s.

Katie found a box.

Katie put the hat on.

Katie opened the box.

Katie saw a hat in the box.

Understanding story sequence

Consonant Blends with l

A **consonant blend** is made up of two or more **consonants**. The **consonants** in the **blend** are called **members**. When you say the **blend** you can hear the sound of each **member**.

The word **<u>bl</u>ue** has the **blend** *bl*.
The word **<u>pl</u>anes** has the **blend** *pl*.
The word **<u>fl</u>y** has the **blend** *fl*.

The **blends** in the sentence below all have the letter l as a **member**.

<u>Bl</u>ue <u>pl</u>anes <u>fl</u>y.

 Circle the **blend** at the beginning of each word.

clock  slide

glove black

Recognizing two-letter initial consonant blends with l

Blend Riddles 1

These pictures show the answers to the riddles below.

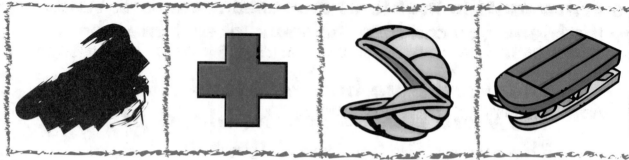

 **Write the answer to each riddle using a blend shown in the box. Then circle the blend you wrote.**

bl	cl	pl	sl

**I am a word
you use in adding.** _____

I am a color. _____

**I am a thing you
ride on snow and ice.** _____

I live in the sea. _____

Writing words using two-letter consonant blends with l

Consonant Blends with r

A **blend** has two or more **consonants**, called **members**.
When you say the **blend**, each **member** can be heard.

The **blends** in the sentence below have **r** as a **member**.

Fred drew a green tree.

 The words in the box have **blends** with **r** as a **member**.
Use them to write the name of each picture below.

| bricks | dragon | crown | grass |

_____

_____

_____

_____

_____

_____

_____

_____

PHONICS & SPELLING

Blend Riddles II

These pictures show the answers to the riddles below.

 Write the answer to each riddle using a **blend** shown in the box. Then circle the **blend** you wrote.

cr	dr	fr	tr

I am green. I croak. _____

I am a bit of rain. _____

I have claws.
I live under water. _____

I rhyme with bee.
I grow in the forest. _____

*Writing words using two-letter initial consonant blends with **r***

Clowning Around

 Each balloon the clown is holding shows a **blend**.
Write the correct **blend** to finish each word.

What thing tells time?

a _____ ock

What is a group of birds?

a _____ ock

What do you use on your hair?

a _____ ush

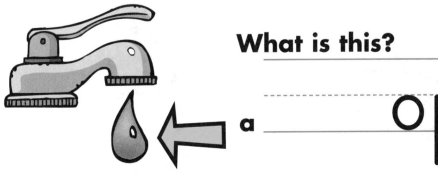

What is this?

a _____ op

Blends With s

A **blend** has two or more **consonants**, called **members**.
When you say the **blend**, each **member** can be heard.

The **blends** in the sentence below
have **s** as a **member**.

This <u>sp</u>ider <u>st</u>ory is <u>sc</u>ary!

 The words in the box have **blends** with s as a **member**.
Use them to write the name of each picture.

| smile | snail | skate | sweater |

_____

- - - - - - - - - - - - - - -

_____

- - - - - - - - - - - - - - -

*Recognizing and writing words using two-letter initial consonant blends with **s***

S and Two Partners

Some **blends** join s with *two* other **consonants**.
You hear the sound of each **member**.

He has **string**, a **spring**, and a **screw**.

 The words in the box have **blends** with s as one **member**. Use them to write the correct word for each picture below.

spray	scrub	strong	straw

_____

_ _ _ _ _ _ _ _ _ _ _ _ _ _

_____

_ _ _ _ _ _ _ _ _ _ _ _ _ _

_____

_ _ _ _ _ _ _ _ _ _ _ _ _ _

_____

_ _ _ _ _ _ _ _ _ _ _ _ _ _

Recognizing and writing words using three-letter initial consonant blends with **s**

Which Word Fits?

 Which word makes sense in each sentence?
Circle the right word in each box.

My bike helmet has a chin ___ .

| scrap | slap | snap | strap |

**The clown will ___ over
his own big feet.**

| drip | slip | strip | trip |

**Look both ways when
you cross the ___ .**

| fleet | sleet | street | sweet |

I ate a ___ of bread.

| price | spice | slice | splice |

A lot of rain falls in ___ .

| swing | spring | string | swing |

*Reading two- and three-letter initial consonant blends with **s***

Watch Out for Blends

 **Read the story by yourself or with someone's help. Underline every word that begins with a blend.**

Green Frog's Wish

Green Frog sat on a lily pad in a pond. She was sad. Blue Bird flew down to the ground.

"Why are you sad, Green Frog?" asked Blue Bird.

"My home is too green!" said Green Frog. "I am green. The plants are green. The water is green. I want more colors!"

"I can try to help you," smiled Blue Bird.

"Yeah!" Green Frog clapped. Blue Bird flew away.

Soon she flew back. She had a red ribbon with a blue stripe. She tied it around a clump of grass. Green Frog smiled.

"Thank you, Blue Bird! You are a good friend!"

Recognizing two- and three-letter initial consonant blends

Green Frog Word Search

 **Find the words in the puzzle below. Circle them.**

ACROSS

ground   grass   try   flew   bird   story   blue

```
F X G G R O U N D
R G R A S S E D C
I F E S T R Y X L
E R E M V C P S A
N O N I Y L L E P
D G F L E U A T P
G F L E W M N H E
B I R D F P T M D
S T O R Y B L U E
```

DOWN

friend

green

smiled

clapped

plant

frog

clump

Identifying words in a word search puzzle

Hearing the Long a Sound

The words lake and train have the long a sound.

lake  train

 Say the names of the two pictures in each box. Circle and color the picture whose name has the long a sound.

Recognizing the long sound of a

Silent e Makes Long a

When the letter **a** is followed by another **consonant** and the letter **e**, it usually takes its long sound, like in the word <u>ape</u>.

When the e helps the **a** this way, it is called **silent** e because it takes no sound.

The word below has **a** followed by the consonant **n**, and then **silent e**.

 X out the **silent e**. Write the new word you see.

 mane

Rewrite the words below and add a silent e after each to make a new word. Say the new word aloud.

pal

mad

rat

tap

*Recognizing and writing words with long **a** spelled **a_e***

Strain Your Brain!

Usually **ai** has the long **a** sound.

n<u>ai</u>l

 **br<u>ai</u>d**

 Write a word from the box to complete each sentence. Circle **ai** in each word you write.

| hail | rain | mail | train | pail | paint | laid | Wait |

The _____ is full of _____ .

Will the  bring _____ or _____ ?

I _____ the _____ on the table.

_____ here for the next _____ .

Another Way to Make Long a

Usually **ay** has the long **a** sound.

h<u>ay</u>   tr<u>ay</u>

 Write a word from the box to complete each sentence. Circle **ay** in each word you write.

| clay | pay | day | play | gray | stay |

_____

Every _____ I

_____ with friends.

_____

I _____ inside when

the clouds are _____ .

Did you _____ for the _____ ?

*Recognizing and writing words with long **a** spelled **ay***

Hearing the Long e Sound

The words weed and meat have the long e sound.

weed   **meat**

 Name the two pictures in each box. Circle and color the picture whose name has the long e sound.

Recognizing the long sound of e

We Keep Up with E

When the only vowel in a word is a single **e** at the end, that e usually takes its long sound.

be   he   she   me   we

Usually, **ee** has the sound of long e.

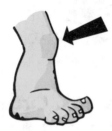 

knee   meet

 Circle the word that completes each sentence.

Spring will ___ here soon.

| be | he | me |

Cars drive on the ___.

| sleep | steep | street |

How far can you ___ ?

| see | seem | sheep |

 **A ___ is on the flower.**

| feet | beef | bee |

I ___ happy today.

| fee | feel | free |

*Recognizing words with long **e** spelled **e** and **ee***

neat!

Usually ea has the sound of long e.

 **l__eaf__**

 **s__ea__l**

 **Write a word from the box to complete each sentence. Circle ea in each word you write.**

| clean | meal | eat | tea | flea | team | leap | cream |

_____   _____

We will _____ our _____ now.

_____

Everyone on the _____

_____

can _____ high.

_____   _____

I put _____ in my _____ .

_____

This _____ likes

_____

to be _____ .

Recognizing and writing words with long e spelled ea

125

PHONICS & SPELLING

Which House Is Mine?

 The words each girl needs to finish what she is saying are on her house. Write the correct word to complete each sentence.

me
we

deep
street

eat
meal

The snow is _____ today.

Cars can't go down the _____ .

I like to _____ hot dogs.

They make a good _____ .

Dad will call _____ soon.

Then _____ will go to the store.

*Reading and completing sentences involving the long **e** sound spelled **e**, **ee**, and **ea***

Make It Long a Today!

 Read the sentence below and look at the numbers over the long a words.

Thank you

1   2   3   4
The gray ape will take the pail.

 Make your own sentence by writing one word from each numbered box on the line with the matching number.

1	2	3	4
fake	whale	save	plane
tame	maid	bake	cake
main	jay	lay	gate
pale	train	paint	tray

1 _____   2 _____

----------------------------   ----------------------------

The _____   _____

3 _____   4 _____

----------------------------   ----------------------------

will _____ the _____ .

Completing sentences to match model; writing words involving the long a sound

127

Greet the Long e Team!

Make your own sentence by writing one word from each numbered box on the line with the matching number.

1	**2**	**3**	**4**
free real mean sleek	team seal eel teen	see heat eat keep	bead heap street meat

1 _____   2 _____

The _____   _____

3 _____   4 _____

will _____ the _____ .

Draw a picture of your long e sentence.

*Completing sentences to match model; writing words involving the long **e** sound*

Month 5 Checklist

Hands-on activities to help your child in school!

PHONICS & SPELLING

Long Vowels: pages 131-133, 135-141, 143-144

Phonics worksheets for this month introduce the long sounds of the vowels *i*, *o*, and *u*. They also present the use of *y* as a vowel, having the sound of either long *e* or long *i*.

❏ Complete the worksheets.
❏ In the long vowel file begun during Month 4, add a tab for each new long vowel spelling pattern as it is introduced. Provide your child with more index cards. On each card, have your child write a different word using the new spelling pattern. Help him or her file the cards correctly.
  ❏ Give your child a yellow highlighter and a page from a newspaper. Ask your child to highlight every word with a particular long vowel spelling pattern, such as *ee*. Then review the words with your child. How many can he or she pronounce correctly?

READING

Comprehension: pages 134, 142, 145
Visual Discrimination: pages 160

Practice in visual discrimination—as in finding objects in a picture—sharpens your child's ability to notice details and thereby identify letters and words rapidly. In addition to the suggestions for comprehension in the Month 4 Checklist, try these activities:

❏ Complete the worksheets.
❏ There are numerous books of hidden pictures, mazes, and other visual puzzles available in grocery, discount, and other stores. Find one appropriate for your child and monitor his or her progress through the book.
❏ Play "I Spy" using riddles to help your child identify an object in plain sight. For example, to describe a clock, you might say, "I spy something white and black." As needed, add hints: "I spy something white and black with hands that tells time."

VOCABULARY & WORD STUDY

Homonyms: pages 147-148

Homonyms are words that sound alike but are spelled differently, such as *made* and *maid*. Even as adults, we enjoy the humor that homonyms often provide in puns, jokes, and riddles. Help your child appreciate this aspect of the English language through these activities:

❑ Complete the worksheets.

❑ Make up a memory game with homonyms. Choose six pairs of homonyms and write each word on a separate index card. Shuffle the cards and lay them face down in rows. Take turns with your child, turning over two cards per turn. If matching homonyms are turned up, the player keeps the cards and takes another turn. If the two cards do not match, return them to their original places and the next player takes a turn. Add more homonyms to make the game more challenging.

GRAMMAR & PUNCTUATION

Sentence Parts: pages 149-154
Nouns: pages 155-158

Grammar is the set of rules governing how we speak and write. When speaking, we can use gestures, facial expressions, and the like to add to what we say. Therefore, we often can get our meaning across without following the rules. However, a writer doesn't have this help, so following grammar rules becomes more important. This month's grammar worksheets focus on the most basic element of grammar-the sentence. They also introduce the idea of the noun, or naming word.

❑ Complete the worksheets.

❑ Encourage your child to answer questions in full sentences, with both a subject and a predicate.

❑ Point out to your child that the name of each thing in the house is a noun. Provide your child with a small pad of self-adhesive note papers and help him or her label household furniture and other objects. Turn the activity into a treasure hunt by sending your child out of the room and hiding a treat under or behind a labeled object. On your child's return, hand him or her a paper on which you have written the name of the object. Have your child read the paper, find the object, and enjoy the treat.

COMPOSITION

Responding to a Picture Prompt: pages 146, 159

Illustrations and text work together to express ideas, particularly in materials aimed for young readers. The composition worksheets for this month encourage your child to draw pictures that add to what he or she writes and to write sentences that add to what is pictured. Help your child become aware of the text-picture connection through these activities:

❑ Complete the worksheets.

❑ Encourage your child to begin thinking like an author. When you read a book together, pause at each page to discuss what your child is learning from the illustration(s) on the page. How do the pictures and words work together to tell a story or explain a process? For example, in a book about butterflies, you might ask, "What do you see in the picture that is not talked about in the words? What do the words tell you that you do not see in the picture?"

Hearing the Long i Sound

The words kite and light have the long i sound.

kite   light

  Say the names of the two pictures in each box. Circle and color the picture that has the long i sound.

Recognizing the long sound of i

131

Mice on a Bike

When the letter **i** is followed by a single **consonant** and the letter e it usually takes its long sound, like in the words m**ice** and b**ike**. The e at the end of the word is silent.

m<u>i</u>c<u>e</u>  b<u>i</u>k<u>e</u>

 Match each word with its picture.

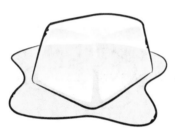

ice

line

bike

dive

file

dice

hive

lime

*Recognizing words with long **i** spelled **i_e***

Like, Lie, Light—All Long i

Usually **ie** has the long **i** sound.

p<u>ie</u>

 t<u>ie</u>

Usually **igh** has the long **i** sound. The **gh** is silent and only the long sound of **i** is heard.

n<u>igh</u>t

 r<u>igh</u>t

---

 In each box, **X** the word that does not have a long **i** sound.

tie fight	die did
~~fit~~	light
lie might	night pie
fin	pin
tight tin	bright tint
nice	sigh

*Recognizing words with long **i** spelled **ie** and **igh***

133

Sentence Sense

**Which word makes sense in each sentence?
Circle the right word in each box.**

My school is a ___ away.

| mile | smile | life | lime |

Can you ___ your laces?

| die | lie | pie | tie |

To have good ___ is to see well.

| high | sigh | sight | slight |

This ___ can fly high.

| bite | dive | kite | time |

The moon is very ___ tonight.

| fight | fright | right | bright |

*Reading and completing short sentences; recognizing words with long **i** sound*

Hearing the Long o Sound

The words nose and coat have the long o sound.

nose

 **coat**

 Say the names of the pictures in each box. Circle and color the picture that has the long o sound.

Recognizing the long sound of o

A Mole in a Robe

When the letter **o** is followed by a single **consonant** and the letter **e** it usually takes its long sound, like in the words **m̲o̲l̲e̲** and **r̲o̲b̲e̲**. The **e** at the end of the word is silent.

m̲o̲l̲e̲   **r̲o̲b̲e̲**

 Match each word with its picture.

rose

doze

hole

pole

rope

cone

stove

nose

*Recognizing words with long **o** spelled **o_e***

O with Partners

Usually, oe at the end of a word has the long o sound.

d<u>oe</u>   h<u>oe</u>

Usually, oa has the long o sound.

c<u>oa</u>st  fl<u>oa</u>t

 Match each word with its picture.

 **toe**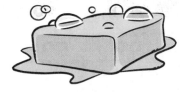

boat

coal

 **toast**

soap

 **coat**

Which Long o Word Fits?

When **o** is at the end of a word it often takes its long sound.

 **"H<u>o</u>, h<u>o</u>, h<u>o</u>!"**

In many words, **ow** has the long **o** sound.

b<u>ow</u>

 **sn<u>ow</u>**

 Circle the long **o** word that completes each sentence.

We will ___ to the store.

no	go	so

A big, black ___ is on the roof.

row	low	crow

Did the wind ___ the tree down?

mow	blow	throw

I like to sleep in my ___ bed.

own	blown	grown

*Recognizing words with long **o** spelled **o** and **ow***

Hearing the Long u Sound

The words mule and fruit have the long u sound.

mule   fruit

  Say the names of the pictures in each box. Circle and color the picture that has the long u sound.

Recognizing the long sound of u

Silent e Makes Long u

When the letter **u** is followed by a single **consonant** and the letter **e** it usually takes its long sound, like in the words **cube** and **huge**. The **e** at the end of the word is silent.

cube

 **huge**

 Match each word with its picture.

rude

dune

flute

prune

cube

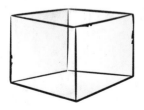

tube

*Recognizing words with long **u** spelled **u_e***

U with Partners

Usually, **ue** has the long **u** sound.

glue

 **Tuesday**

In some words, **ui** has the long **u** sound.

fruit

 **juice**

 Match each word with its picture.

blue

clue

glue

bruise

cruise

suit

Which Word?

 Circle the word that best completes each sentence.

I can play a ___ on my flute.

tune	rule	use

Put on your best ___ to go to the play.

juice	fruit	suit

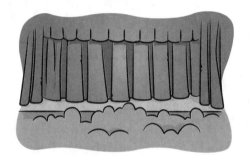

Want to go for a ___ ride?

prune	hue	mule

Is that story ___ or made up?

blue	glue	true

Mom put an ice ___ in my glass.

clue	cube	cruise

*Reading and completing short sentences; recognizing words with the long **u** sound*

Y as a Vowel

The letter **y** can be used as a vowel as well as a consonant.
Sometimes it has the long **i** sound, as in **fl<u>y</u>**.

fl<u>y</u>

Sometimes it has the long **e** sound as in **happ<u>y</u>**.

happ<u>y</u>

 Read each word aloud. If the word uses the long **i** sound, write **i** on the line. If it uses the long **e** sound, write **e**.

cry _____

fry _____

silly _____

family _____

city _____

hydrant _____

*Recognizing the two vowel sounds of **y**: long **i** and long **e***

Tracking Down Vowel Sounds

 **Read the sentences below. Each sentence has two words that use y as a vowel.**

If the y sounds like long **i**, draw a ◯ around the word.

If the y sounds like long **e**, draw a ▢ around the word.

My family is big.

The sky is pretty.

That baby can cry!

It is easy to fry an egg.

The plant is very dry.

Why is he sleepy?

*Recognizing the two vowel sounds of **y**: long **i** and long **e***

Three Friends, Three Homes

The words each boy needs to finish what he is saying are on his house. Write the correct words to complete each sentence.

**bright
drove
true**

**try
cute
so**

**pie
juice
toast**

"In the morning I ate _____ and _____ . Tonight I want _____ ."

"My baby sister is _____ _____ .

I _____ to take care of her."

"I _____ to a _____ star.

Do you think that is _____ ?"

Reading and completing sentences

145

Ready to Rhyme?

Each rhyme below is missing one word. Write one word from the box that would best finish each rhyme.

bone	high	fruit	moan	so	cute	my	snow

If you fall over that stone, _____

_____

we will soon hear you _____ .

Does a monkey in a suit _____

_____

look silly or _____ ?

I want to go _____

_____

and play in the _____ .

I wish I could fly! _____

_____

I would fly so _____ .

Completing rhymes

Sound Alikes

Homonyms are words that sound alike, but do not have the same spelling or meaning. **Pear** and **pair** are **homonyms**.

pear     **pair**

 Match each word with its **homonym**.

 **sun**

rode

 **meet**

sale

 **road**

son

 **sail**

tale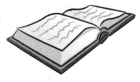

 tail

meat

Hidden Homonyms

Homonyms are words that sound alike, but do not have the same spelling or meaning.

 Color the spaces that have two **homonyms** .
Color the spaces that do not have two **homonyms** .

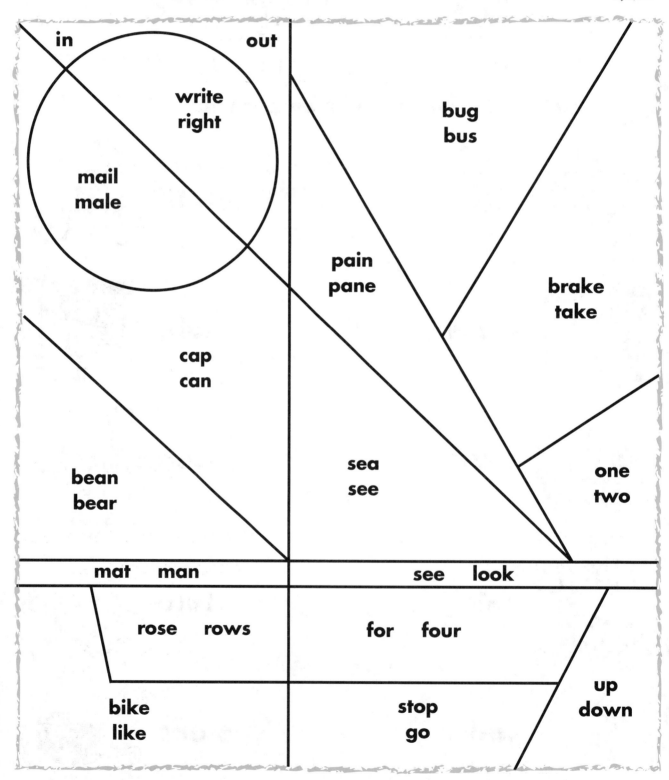

in   out

write
right

bug
bus

mail
male

pain
pane

brake
take

cap
can

bean
bear

sea
see

one
two

mat   man   see   look

rose   rows   for   four

bike
like

stop
go

up
down

Recognizing homonyms

Sentence Fun

Every sentence has two parts. One part names who or what is being told about. That is the **naming part**. One part tells what a person or thing does or is. That is the **action part**.

The cat   **plays with yarn.**

naming part   action part

 Draw a line to match each **naming part** with an **action part**. Read each sentence you make.

Naming Parts	**Action Parts**
The girls	bark loudly.
Snow	is tall.
My father	is falling on the tree.
The dogs	are best friends.

Recognizing the naming part (subject) and the action part (predicate) in a sentence

149

A Trip to the Airport

The **naming part** of a sentence names who or what is being told about. Another word for **naming part** is **subject**. More than one word might be used for the **subject**.

<u>The pilot</u> wears a blue suit.
subject

<u>Lots of pilots</u> wear blue suits.
subject

 Underline the **subject** in each sentence. Remember that more than one word might be used for the **subject**.

Many people come to the airport.

Mom holds the tickets.

The little boy pulls a suitcase.

People in the airport walk fast.

Identifying the complete subject

Race Track Action

The **action part** of a sentence tells what the **subject** is or is doing. Another word for **action part** is **predicate**. More than one word may be used for the **predicate**.

Many cars <u>race</u>.
predicate

Many cars <u>race around the track</u>.
predicate

 Underline the **predicate** in each sentence. Remember that more than one word might be used for the **predicate**.

The cars race in a circle.

One car stops for gas.

Some workers change the tires.

The fastest car wins.

At the Beach

The sentences below are missing parts. Write one sentence part from the box to complete each sentence. Then write **s** in the ☐ if you added a **subject** or **p** if you added a **predicate**.

Birds	The sun	swim in the sea	finds a shell

☐ _____

_____ **shines brightly.**

☐ **Happy fish** _____

_____ .

☐ **A girl with red hair** _____

_____ .

☐ _____

_____ **fly in the sky.**

Completing sentences with subjects or predicates

Silly Sentences Game

Cut out the **subject** cards and the **predicate** cards. Put them in two piles. Pick up one **subject** card and one **predicate** card at a time. Put the cards together and read the silly sentence they make.

Subject cards:

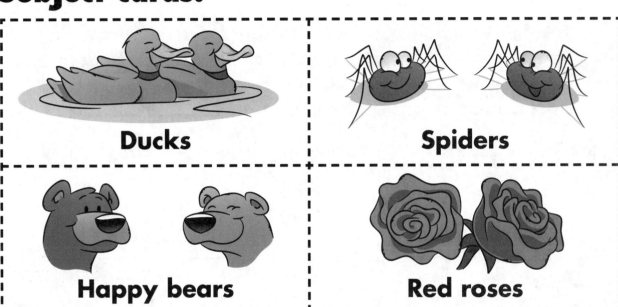

Ducks

Spiders

Happy bears

Red roses

Predicate cards:

spin webs.

smell nice.

wear fur coats.

quack loudly.

Matching subjects and predicates to form sentences

Silly Sentences Game

Spiders | smell nice.

Roses | quack loudly.

Subject   Subject

Subject   Subject

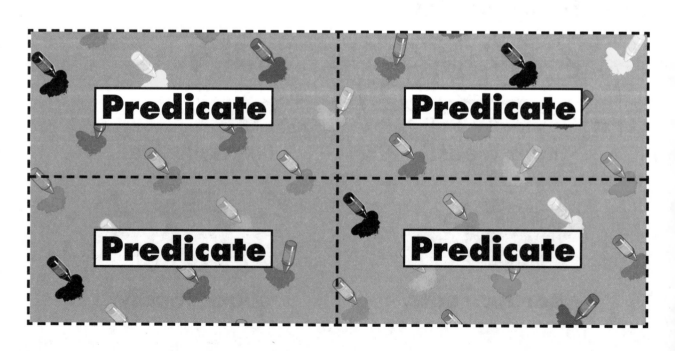

Predicate   Predicate

Predicate   Predicate

Matching subjects and predicates to form sentences

It Has a Name!

A word that names a person, place, or thing is called a noun.

mother
person

home
place

purse
thing

My mother went to our home to get her purse.

 Write one **noun** from the box to name each picture below.

shop	car	bug	hat	girl	barn

The First Day of School

 Write a noun from the box to complete each sentence.

teacher	school	bell	pencil	desks

The boys and girls are at _____.

The _____ smiles at the children.

The girls and boys sit at _____.

The _____ rings at noon.

Ann writes with a _____.

Using nouns to complete sentences

Which Ones Are Nouns?

Nouns are words that name people, places, and things.

 Circle the **nouns** in the word box.

hen	farmer	barn	works	if
and	green	fence	sun	tree

 Draw a picture of one of the **nouns** from the box in the space below. Write the **noun** below the picture.

Searching for nouns

 Circle all the **nouns** in each sentence below.

The turtle lives in a pond.

The monkey has a tail.

The giraffe eats leaves.

The zebras have stripes.

The pilot sees an eagle.

Ants make hills.

Identifying nouns in sentences

Outside Games

Write two sentences about your favorite games to play outside. You can use words from the box below.

ball	bat	friends	rope
jump	kick	run	throw

Sentence 1

_____

- -

_____

- -

_____

Sentence 2

_____

- -

_____

- -

_____

Where Are the Keys?

How many s can you find in this picture?

Circle each one you find.

Circle how many s you found.

12 Perfect!   **8 or 9** Good job!

10 or 11 Great!   **7 or below** Keep trying!

Visual discrimination

Month 6 Checklist

Hands-on activities to help your child in school!

PHONICS & SPELLING

Consonant Blends: pages 163-164, 166
Consonant Digraphs: pages 167-173

In a consonant blend, the sound usually associated with each member consonant is heard. For example, in *strawberry*, the sounds of *s*, *t*, and *r* are all heard. However, in a consonant digraph, the two letters together stand for a single new sound—one that is different from any of the sounds usually associated with the letters. For example, in *shell*, the beginning sound (the consonant digraph *sh*) has no hint of either *s* or *h*. Phonics worksheets in this month focus on blends and digraphs at both beginnings and endings of words.

❑ Complete the worksheets.

❑ A fun way to become aware of final blends (blends at the ends of words) is to make up simple rhymes. Say a word that ends in a blend, such as *lift* or *drink*, and have your child come up with as many rhymes for the word as possible (e.g., *lift, sift, drift; drink, ink, blink, sink, wink*). Then together make up a rhyme using two or more of these words—for example, "You will blink and I will wink."

❑ To help your child become aware of the two sounds of *th*, have your child place a hand on his or her throat while saying words with the (voiced) sound of *th* in *this, those, that,* and *mother*. A voiced sound is made when using both a mouth position and the vocal cords to pronounce a sound. Make sure your child feels the slight vibration of the vocal cords. Then contrast this feeling with the lack of vibration inside the throat when saying words with the (unvoiced) sound of *th* in *thin, thick, thirty,* and *throw*. An unvoiced sound is made when using a mouth position, but not the vocal cords to pronounce a sound.

READING

Comprehension: pages 165, 174
Main Idea: pages 185-188
Details: pages 189
Sequence: pages 190

In this month's worksheets, your child learns that the main idea of a piece of writing is its most important idea. In a well written paragraph, story, or description, all details relate to that main idea and help make it clear. Help your child develop his or her ability to identify and focus on a main idea with these activities:

❑ Complete the worksheets.

❑ After listening to a short announcement on television or radio, such as a weather advisory or commercial, ask your child to identify the main idea of the announcement. As he or she gains more skill at naming the main idea, invite your child to identify one detail stated in the announcement that supports its main idea. For example, after a commercial for cars, your child could state that the main idea is that listeners should buy a car from that dealer. A detail might be that the prices are low.

161

GRAMMAR & PUNCTUATION

Nouns: pages 175-178
Verbs: pages 179-184

During this month, your child learns more about nouns, such as: what proper nouns are; how they are capitalized; and how to make most nouns name more than one item by adding *s*. In addition, several worksheets introduce the concept of verbs and how they are used in sentences. Special attention is given to the present tense forms of the verb *to be—is, am,* and *are*.

❏ Complete the worksheets.
❏ Be careful to model correct grammar when speaking with or around your child. Since your child patterns his or her speech after yours, make an effort to observe the grammar rules about agreement in number between subjects and verbs that are taught on the worksheets.
❏ Encourage your child to use interesting verbs in his or her own speech. For example, instead of *go*, your child might use any of these more precise words: *walk, run, stroll, wiggle, hurry, gallop, skip*. Make a list of frequently used words such as *say* and *go*, and post the list on the refrigerator door for easy reference.

COMPOSITION

Writing a Story: pages 191-192

Today, many teachers help their students organize ideas for writing stories and reports by using graphic organizers. A graphic organizer is a graph, table, or diagram that shows connections between ideas. Seeing ideas in picture or table form is particularly useful for visual learners. This workbook provides a variety of graphic organizers for writing. The first of these organizers appears in this month's pages; it will aid your child in developing ideas for an original story.

❏ Complete the worksheets.
❏ If your child has difficulty thinking of a topic for the original story, have him or her turn to pages 379 and 380. Pictures on these pages are provided as story starters.
❏ If the space provided on page 192 is not enough for your child's story, or your child has more stories to tell, make sure he or she has access to additional writing paper. Collect the stories in a folder to show friends and relatives, and to serve as a record of your child's progress.

Blend or Brend?

A consonant blend has two or more consonants, called members. When you say the blend, each member can be heard.

<u>p</u><u>l</u>ay = <u>p</u> + <u>l</u> + ay

 Circle each word that begins with the wrong blend. Rewrite it using the correct blend.

Those gleen beans grow fast.

_____

_____

Jan will shop at the snore.

_____

_____

The letter is flom my friend.

_____

_____

Ron will bling his pet spider.

_____

_____

A Blend at the End

A word may begin or end with a blend.

skate   **mask**

 Underline the two-consonant blend at the end of each word.

lift	and	tent	fast
best	think	ant	stamp
sent	kind	last	bank
ask	tilt	must	lamp

 Write four of the ending blends you underlined.

_____ _____ _____ _____

Use the words above to write the name for each picture.

 _____   _____

Recognizing consonant blends in final position

The Perfect Ending

Circle the word that is missing in each sentence.

Bob put a ___ over his face.

> mask   mast

I will ___ you a letter.

> send   sent

Make a ___ of things to buy.

> lint   list

An ___ is on my cookie!

> and   ant

We will sleep in a ___ at camp.

> tent   test

A ___ is a baby horse.

> cold   colt

Help me ___ my lost book.

> find   fist

A Great Tank

Read the word on each fish.
If the word begins with a blend, color the fish 🐟.
If the word ends with a blend, color it 🐟. If the
word begins and ends with a blend, color it 🐟.

Reviewing consonant blends in initial and final positions

Check Out ch

ch has the sound you hear at the beginning of **chair** and at the end of **branch**.

chair

 **branch**

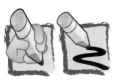 Write **ch** to complete the words.
Match each word with its picture.

_____eck

ben_____

_____est

tea_____er

_____ain

in_____

_____ief

 _____ur_____

*Recognizing the sound of the consonant digraph **ch***

Showing Off sh

sh has the sound you hear at the beginning of <u>sh</u>oe and at the end of fi<u>sh</u>.

shoe   fish

 Write **sh** to complete the words.
Match each word with its picture.

_____**irt**

di_____

fla_____

bu_____

_____**apes**

tra_____

_____**op**

_____**ark**

*Recognizing the sound of the consonant digraph **sh***

Two Sounds of th

th has the sound you hear in the words <u>the</u> and mo<u>th</u>er.
th also has the sound you hear in the words <u>th</u>irty and tee<u>th</u>.

mo<u>th</u>er

 **tee<u>th</u>**

 Read each word aloud. If the word uses the **th** sound as in **mother**, draw a line from the word to the mother. If the word uses the **th** sound as in **thirty**, draw a line from the word to the 30.

thing

thin

there

then

thick

bath

father

with

*Recognizing the two sounds of the consonant digraph **th**: voiced and unvoiced*

What's Up with wh?

wh has the sound you hear at the
beginning of **wh**eel.

 **Read each sentence.
Draw a line to the missing wh word.**

whale
what
wheat
where
which
while
white

The girls sat ____ they ate.

A ____ lives in the sea.

Some farmers grow winter ____.

The old TV show is in black and ___.

And then ____ happened?

I wonder ____ my dog went.

Can you tell ____ answer is right?

Recognizing the sound of the consonant digraph **wh**

Smile for the Photo

ph has the same sound as **f**.

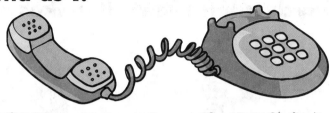

<u>ph</u>one

  Underline the **ch**, **sh**, **th**, or **ph** in each word.
Circle the word that names the picture.

author		shovel	
alphabet		elephant	
pheasant		bench	
cheese		whistle	
trophy		gopher	
tooth		inch	

 Write **ph** to finish the word below.
Read the word aloud.

___ o t o

*Recognizing the sound of the consonant digraph **ph**; reviewing consonant digraphs*

Can You Hear gh?

In some words, **gh** has the sound of **f**.
In other words, **gh** is silent—it makes no sound.

laugh     **light**

 Underline the word with **gh** in each sentence. If the **gh** has the sound of **f**, write **f** above the word. If it's silent, circle the word.

She has a cold with a cough.

The plane flew up high.

Turn the car to the right.

Tree bark feels rough, not smooth.

The boy will go all the way through the tunnel.

*Recognizing the consonant digraph **gh** as silent or with the sound of **f***

Using ng

ng has the sound you hear at the end of **ki<u>ng</u>** and **ba<u>ng</u>**.

bang

king

Write **ng** to complete the words.
Match each word with its picture.

wi_____

ri_____

swi_____

wro_____

fi_____er

si_____

Some__ing's Missi__

 Read the story, or ask someone to help you. Some words have a pair of letters missing. Use the letter pairs in the box to complete those words.

| ch | sh | th | wh | gh | ph | ng |

Bear sat in a ____air. The tele____one began to

ri____. It was Bear's friend, ____imp. "A ____eel

fell off my bike!" said ____imp. "I ____ink I can

fix it," said Bear. "I will come over to your house."

"____en?" asked ____imp. "Ri____t now!" said Bear.

"I will bri____ my tools." It took Bear only a ____or

time to fix the ____eel. "____is ____eel is on nice

and ti____t now," said Bear.

"____ank you!" said ____imp

and he ____ook Bear's hand.

Reading comprehension; completing words with missing digraphs

A Name for Everyone

A **proper noun** is the name of an exact person, place, or thing. Every **proper noun** begins with a capital letter. Your name is a proper noun.

<u>F</u>luffy     **<u>G</u>ina**

 Write a name for each picture. You can use the names in the box or make up your own.

| Ben | Lia | Kim | Ted | Bud | Ruff | Misty |

_____

_____

_____

_____

Writing Proper Nouns

A **proper noun** is the name of an exact person, place, or thing. Every **proper noun** begins with a capital letter.

United States

 **June**

 Read each sentence and rewrite the **proper noun** that is not written correctly.

The train goes to boston.

_____

- - - - - - - - - - - - - - - -

_____

 maria ran home fast.

_____

- - - - - - - - - - - - - - - -

_____

This man lives in japan.

_____

- - - - - - - - - - - - - - - -

_____

ken rides a red bike.

_____

- - - - - - - - - - - - - - - -

_____

Recognizing and writing proper nouns

How Many?

To make many nouns mean "more than one," add **s** at the end. Adding **s** makes a **plural noun**.

one bear

three bears

 Look at the picture and then read the questions below. Circle the answer to each question.

Look for a cap. How many do you see?

| one cap | two caps | three caps |

Look for a rope. How many do you see?

| one rope | two ropes | three ropes |

Look for a mat. How many do you see?

| one mat | two mats | three mats |

Look for a ball. How many do you see?

| one ball | two balls | three balls |

*Forming plurals of regular nouns by adding **s***

Animal or Animals

  Read the word under each picture.
If it's a **plural noun**, write it on the Animals list.
If it's not, write it on the Animal list.

birds

pig

cats

lion

dogs

tiger

Animal | Animals

Recognizing plural nouns

What Is a Verb?

A verb is a word that tells what a person or thing does.

run     spin

 Draw a line to match each picture with its verb.

march

sing

dance

clap

Circle the verb that completes each sentence.

The bell _____ at noon.

| loud | rings |

The cat _____ on my lap.

| purrs | friend |

Recognizing verbs

Where Is the Verb?

A verb is a word that tells
what a person or thing does.

The sun shines.

 Circle the **verb** in each sentence below.

Boats sail on the sea.

A woman sits in the sun.

Waves come to the shore.

The girls play a game.

The boy throws a ball.

Recognizing verbs within sentences

Bears in Space

A **verb** usually ends in **s** when it tells about only one person or thing. A **verb** usually does not end in **s** when it tells about more than one person or thing.

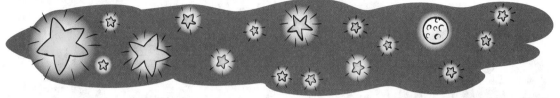

The star twinkle_s_.   **Stars twinkle.**

 Read each sentence. Circle the correct verb to complete it.

The little bear _____ a spacesuit.

wear	wears

Bears _____ into space today.

go	goes

The big bears _____ into the spaceship.

get	gets

The big bears _____ pictures.

take	takes

The little bear _____ into the spaceship.

get	gets

The little bear _____ out of the spaceship.

go	goes

Which Is Correct?

 Fill in the ◯ by the sentence that uses the correct **verb**.

◯ **The boys and girls like art class.**
◯ **The boys and girls likes art class.**

◯ **The girl paint a picture.**
◯ **The girl paints a picture.**

◯ **One boy makes a clay bird.**
◯ **One boy make a clay bird.**

◯ **Some boys draws cars.**
◯ **Some boys draw cars.**

◯ **The teacher pins the pictures on the board.**
◯ **The teacher pin the pictures on the board.**

◯ **The pictures stay up for weeks.**
◯ **The pictures stays up for weeks.**

Choosing the correct forms of verbs to agree with singular or plural subjects

Am, Are and Is

Sometimes, **verbs** also tell what someone or something is. We use three words to tell what someone or something is: **am**, **are**, and **is**.

Verb Chart

I	am
You	are
He, She, or It	is
We	are
They	are

When you are telling about yourself and using the word I, use **am**.

I **am** happy!

When you are telling about one other person or thing, but not using the word you, use **is**.

He **is** happy!

When you are telling about more than one or using the word you, use **are**.

Are **you** happy?

The dogs **are** happy!

Write **am**, **are**, or **is** to complete each sentence.

Leaves _____ green.   I _____ smart.

Nan _____ a girl.   This peach _____ sweet.

We _____ friends.   You _____ happy.

*Recognizing the present tense conjugation of the verb **to be***

How Smart Are You?

Fill in the ○ by the sentence that uses the correct verb.

○ I am your friend.
○ I is your friend.

○ You is the winner!
○ You are the winner!

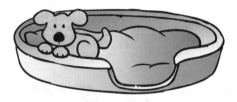

○ Brian are the star of the team.
○ Brian is the star of the team.

○ The puppy is tiny.
○ The puppy are tiny.

○ We is tired at bedtime.
○ We are tired at bedtime.

Recognizing the present tense conjugation of the verb **to be**

That's the Idea!

The main idea of a story is its most important idea.

 The pictures below tell a story. Underline the sentence that tells the main idea.

The birthday party was fun.   **Jason got a bike for his birthday.**

No one had fun at the party.   **Jason's cake was big.**

Sue gave away three kittens.   **Sue does not like kittens.**

Sue kept all the kittens.   **The kittens were gray.**

Identifying the main idea of a story told in pictures

Choosing the Main Idea

The **main idea** of a story is its most important idea.

 Read each story. Circle the sentence that tells the **main idea.**

Tracy sees that it is raining. She puts on boots. She puts on a raincoat. She puts on a hat. Now she is ready.

Tracy dresses for a rainy day.

Tracy takes a long time to get ready.

Paint is coming off the old house. The windows are broken. The front door is loose. The roof has big holes.

The old house is nice.

The old house needs to be fixed.

Identifying the main idea

What Does Not Belong?

The pictures below tell more about the main idea. Cross out the picture that does not belong.

Identifying pictures that do not relate to the main ideas

Reading Paragraphs

A paragraph is a group of sentences that tell about a **main idea**.

 Cross out the sentence in each **paragraph** that does not belong.

The pond is a noisy place.
The frogs croak. The geese
honk. I like ice cream. The flies buzz.

Hal has a bad cold. His head hurts.
He sneezes a lot. He feels cold and
then hot. Hal plays the flute.

We went to the circus today. Dogs are
good pets. We saw the lion act. The
clowns were funny.

Identifying irrelevant sentences in paragraphs

Story Memory

 Read the story.

    A boy named Jim had three dogs. The names of the dogs were Tip, Jed, and Bud.

    Tip liked to eat meat. Jed liked to hide bones. Bud liked to play ball.

    Jim fed Tip meat. He gave Jed a bone. He played ball with Bud.

    The dogs loved Jim and he loved his dogs.

 Circle the answer to each question.

What did Bud like to do?

play ball	eat meat

What did the boy give Jed?

a bone	a ball

The names of the dogs were Jed, Bud, and ____.

Jim	Tip

Recalling details in a story

Make a Wish!

 The sentences below tell a story, but they are all mixed up. Number them from 1 to 5 in the correct order.

_____ **Kevin rode away on his new bike.**

_____ **The little man ate the food and told Kevin to make a wish.**

_____ **One day Kevin met a hungry little man.**

_____ **Kevin wished for a new bike.**

_____ **Kevin gave the little man some food.**

Understanding story sequence

Your own Story, Part 1

Make up your own story. Think of what happens first, next, and last.

 Draw three pictures to tell your own story. Use the boxes to show what happens first, next, and last.

First

Next

Last

Your Own Story, Part 2

You have made a picture plan. Now write the story. Write a title at the top to give your story a name. Use the rest of the page to write the words to your story.

Title

Writing an original story

Month 7 Checklist

Hands-on activities to help your child in school!

PHONICS & SPELLING

Vowels (*r*-controlled and others): pages 195-197, 199

Often, the sound of a vowel is affected by the consonant that immediately follows it. One example of this is in the *r*-controlled vowels, such as *ar* in *car*, *or* in *corn*, and *er*, *ir*, *ur* as in *her*, *fir*, and *curl*. In addition to the various sounds of *r*-controlled vowels, this month's phonics worksheets look at the vowel sound of *al* as in *walk* and *aw* as in *paw*.

❑ Complete the worksheets.
❑ Make a set of cards for a memory game involving the four vowel sounds learned this month. On index cards, write four words for each of these sounds: (1) *ar* as in *farm*; (2) *or* as in *fork*; (3) the *aw* sound, represented by *aw* as in *paw*, and in a very similar way, by *al* as in *call* and *walk*; and (4) the vowel sound heard in *bird* and represented by *er*, *ir*, *or*, *ur*, and sometimes *ar* and *ear*. Shuffle the cards, lay them out face down, and take turns turning over two cards at a time. Anyone who turns over two cards with matching vowel sounds keeps the cards and takes another turn. Anyone who turns over non-matching cards returns them to their places.

READING

Reading Comprehension: pages 198, 200-201
Reading for Detail: pages 202, 215-216
Fact and Opinion: pages 217-218
Visual Discrimination: pages 224

Reading worksheets for this month give practice in reading for detail. They also introduce the difference between fact and opinion—an essential critical thinking skill.

❑ Complete the worksheets.
❑ Develop memory and attention to detail by showing your child a tray filled with a variety of small objects, such as a pencil, spoon, button, etc. Have him or her view the assortment for about 20 seconds, and then hide it. Have your child recall as many items as possible, with as much detail as possible (the color of the pencil, for example). When your child has named all he or she can remember, display the tray a second time both to verify what was listed and to see what was missed. At some later time, repeat the activity with different items.
❑ One of the worksheets pairs statements—one fact and one opinion—about the same topics. Apply this approach in conversation. For example, you state a fact: "The store is open." Have your child respond with an opinion about the store, such as "I enjoy shopping at this store" or "This store has good things to buy."

GRAMMAR & PUNCTUATION

Word Order in Sentences: pages 203-204
Verbs and Nouns; Plural and Irregular Nouns: pages 205-206, 207-214
Kinds of Sentences: pages 219-221

These activities will help your child master basic elements of grammar:

❏ Complete the worksheets.
❏ To reinforce the idea that word order is important in sentences, pause periodically when reading a story to your child. Reread a sentence, change the word order, and ask if the sentence still makes sense. For example, the sentence "Goldilocks ate the porridge" will not make sense when changed to "The porridge ate Goldilocks." However, rearranging "Goldilocks saw the bears" to "The bears saw Goldilocks" results in a sensible sentence, although the meaning has changed.
❏ Help your child identify places in the house where things are stored, such as a cupboard for dishes, a box for toys, a jar for cookies, and a holder for toothbrushes. Give him or her notepaper and tape, or a pad of stick-on notes. Have your child make a label for each of these storage areas, listing what is kept there. Make sure that your child uses the correct plural form of each item's name (dishes, toys, cookies, toothbrushes).

COMPOSITION

Writing Statements and Questions: pages 222-223

Use these activities to give your child practice in writing original sentences.

❏ Complete the worksheets.
❏ Have your child cut out magazine photographs or illustrations showing a person. Ask him or her to paste the picture on writing paper and then write a sentence (statement or question) underneath the picture that the person in the picture might say.
❏ As a variation of the above activity, have your child find a picture showing two people. Give your child two index cards—one card showing a period and the other a question mark. Help your child verbally develop a conversation that the people in the picture might have, holding up the correct index card while saying each sentence in the conversation.

Are You Ready for ar?

Usually, **ar** has the vowel sound in **barn**.

b<u>ar</u>n

 Circle the correct name for each picture.

aim   arm   pack   park   star   stay

make   mark   cat   cart   party   pantry

 **The opposite for each of these words has ar in it.
Write each opposite.**

near _____   finish _____

soft _____   light _____

*Recognizing the sounds of **r**-controlled vowels*

Don't Forget or!

Usually, **or** has the vowel sound in **f<u>or</u>k**.

f<u>or</u>k

 Circle the correct name for each picture.

cook   cork

orange   otter

stork   stock

hose   horse

stare   store

corn   cone

 Draw lines to match each **or** word with its opposite.

more   tall

north   less

short   after

before   south

*Recognizing the sounds of **r**-controlled vowels*

The Early Bird Gets the Worm

The vowel sound is the same in each of the words below.

b<u>ir</u>d　　**w<u>or</u>m**　　**t<u>ur</u>n**　　**f<u>er</u>n**　　**<u>ear</u>th**

The ar in backward also has this vowel sound.

backw<u>ar</u>d

 Write five different letter pairs that can have the same vowel sound as you hear in <u>earth</u>.

_____　　_____

_____　　_____

_____　　_____

 Circle the words that have the same vowel sound as you hear in <u>earth</u>.

nurse　　**germ**　　**four**　　**forward**

hear　　**more**　　**girl**　　**tear**

Recognizing the sounds of r-controlled vowels

This Word or That?

 Write a word from the box to complete each sentence so it makes sense.

farm	or	dirt	storm	burn	her	work	herd

Many chickens live on that _____ .

A tree fell during the wind _____ .

Stay in the shade or the sun will _____ **you.**

A _____ **of cows stood in the field.**

*Reading and completing sentences with words containing **r**-controlled vowels*

Different Letters, Same Sound

Usually, aw has the vowel sound you hear in saw.

saw

Often, al has the same kind of sound.

call   talk

 Write a word from the box to name each picture.

| lawn | ball | yawn | salt | walk | paw | walnut | hawk |

_____

- - - - - - - - - - - -

_____

_____

- - - - - - - - - - - -

_____

_____

- - - - - - - - - - - -

_____

_____

- - - - - - - - - - - -

_____

Recognizing vowel sounds of a/consonant combinations

Aw, How Cute!

Write a word from the box to complete each sentence so it makes sense.

salt	crawl	lawn	jaw	walnut
small	chalk	law	claw	straw

That _____ panda is cute.

The shell of this _____ is very hard.

A crook is someone who breaks the _____.

Do not put too much _____ on your food.

Paul used _____ to write on the sidewalk.

*Reading and completing sentences with words containing **a**/consonant combinations*

Early Call

 Read Bob's story.

This morning I
woke up early. It was
still dark. I heard a bird sing
far away. Soon more birds started to call
out. I walked to the window. The sky began to
turn light. I saw the sun rise.

 Circle the words in the story with the same vowel
sound as **barn**.

 Draw a box around the words with the same vowel
sound as **all** and **law**. Underline the words with the
same vowel sound as **fork**.

 Write three words from the story with the same
vowel sound as **girl**, **nurse**, and **earth**.

ir	ur	ear

Sharing Ideas

 Read Bob's story again on page 201, then turn back to this page and follow the directions.

 Draw what Bob heard first.

 Draw what Bob saw.

 Read the sentences below. Write T on the line if the sentence is true. Write F if it is false.

_____ **Bob saw the sun rise.**   _____ **Bob heard a dog bark.**

_____ **Bob stayed up all night.**

Recalling details in a story

More Silly Sentences

The order of words in a sentence is important. If you change the order, you can change what the sentence means.

Alex loves Rover.

Rover loves Alex.

Cut out each of the small cards and then the list of verbs. Place the small cards face down in a pile. Then pick two cards. Place one before any verb in the list. Place the other after the verb. Read the sentence you have made. Then switch the cards. Read this sentence, too. Repeat with other cards and other verbs.

Verbs

a cat	a mouse	catches
Dana	Joe	sees
a lion	a snail	scares
the mother	the baby	hugs
Mike	Robin	chases
the bird	the frog	helps

Understanding the importance of word order in sentences

Let's Go to the Zoo!

Write a noun or a verb from the box to complete each sentence.

ape	bear	made	went	were

_____ **verb** _____

We _____ to the zoo.

_____ **noun** _____

I waved to the _____ .

_____ **verb** _____

The monkeys _____ me laugh.

_____ **noun** _____

The _____ was asleep.

_____ **verb** _____

The hippos _____ fat.

Completing sentences with nouns and verbs

Let's Go to the Movies!

Write a noun or a verb from the box to complete each sentence.

box	buy	is	meet	seats

verb

Rita and Tom _____ at the door.

verb

They _____ tickets to a movie.

noun

They buy a _____ of popcorn.

noun

They choose _____ in front.

verb

The movie _____ funny.

Completing sentences with nouns and verbs

Not Just One

A plural noun names "more than one." Add **es** to a noun ending in **s**, **x**, **ch**, or **sh** to make it plural.

one dress **two dress<u>es</u>** **one fox** **two fox<u>es</u>**

 Rewrite each **noun**, adding **es** to make it **plural**.

match

_____

- - - - - - - - - - - -

_____

bus

_____

- - - - - - - - - - - -

_____

brush

_____

- - - - - - - - - - - -

_____

box

_____

- - - - - - - - - - - -

_____

Adding **-es** to form plurals of nouns ending in **s**, **x**, **ch**, and **sh**

One and More Than One

**Read each noun printed in red.
Circle its correct plural form.**

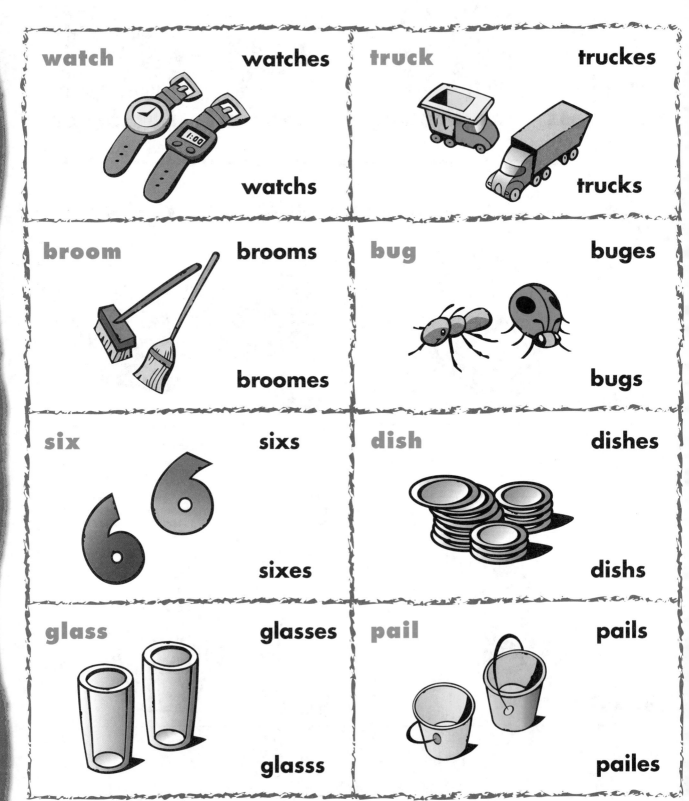

watch	watches	truck	truckes
	watchs		trucks
broom	brooms	bug	buges
	broomes		bugs
six	sixs	dish	dishes
	sixes		dishs
glass	glasses	pail	pails
	glasss		pailes

Recognizing the plural forms of nouns

Watch Out for y

Some nouns end in **y** after a consonant.
To make these nouns plural, change the **y** to **i** and add **es**.

one bunny   bunn**i**~~y~~ + es = bunnies   two bunnies

 Rewrite each noun to make it plural.

candy

fly

baby

berry

kitty

lady

*Forming plurals of nouns ending in **y** after a consonant*

Making Plurals

**Read each noun printed in red.
Circle its correct plural form.**

daisy daisies  daisys	**cherry** cherries  cherryes
lunch lunchs  lunches	**fly** flies  flyes
fox foxs  foxes	**city** cityes  cities
chick chickes  chicks	**puppy** puppies  puppys

Recognizing the plural forms of nouns

noun Search

Read the nouns and their plural forms in the box.
Circle each of them in the puzzle below.

| ball | baby | box | snake | inch | fly |
| balls | babies | boxes | snakes | inches | flies |

a	b	a	l	l	e	f	z
b	o	x	e	s	h	l	v
a	s	f	b	o	x	y	b
b	n	j	i	n	c	h	a
i	a	f	l	i	e	s	l
e	k	b	a	b	y	d	l
s	e	i	n	c	h	e	s
x	s	n	a	k	e	w	u

Special Plurals
Some nouns have a special plural form.

One	More Than One
man	men
woman	women
child	children
mouse	mice
foot	feet
tooth	teeth

Read each sentence and the noun next to it in blue. Write the plural form of each noun to complete each sentence.

I put socks on my _____. **foot**

Both _____ can swim. **child**

The _____ like the maze. **mouse**

Two _____ wrote the song. **man**

I brush my _____. **tooth**

Three _____ baked pies. **woman**

Recognizing irregular plurals

More Special Plurals

A few nouns do not change in their plural form.

One	More Than One
deer	deer
fish	fish
moose	moose
scissors	scissors
sheep	sheep

Look at the picture clues.
Write the missing plural noun in each sentence.

_____

Many _____ live in the park.

Luis saw two _____ in the woods.

_____

The _____ eat grass.

Feed the _____ before lunch.

_____

We use _____ to cut paper.

Recognizing irregular plurals

Crossword Fun

Read the clues, then fill in the crossword puzzle.

ACROSS

2. The plural of **baby**
4. The plural of **shop**
5. The plural of **deer**

DOWN

1. The plural of **man**
2. The plural of **box**
3. The plural of **brush**

Plural noun review

Fun on the Farm

Look at the picture, then circle the answer to each question.

What color is the barn?

yellow   red   blue

Which animal is sleeping?

cat   horse   dog

How many eggs are in the nest?

two   three   four

Where are the flowers growing?

by the fence   under the tree   by the barn

Ann Rides the Bus

 Read Ann's story.

It is fun to shop in the city. Mom and I get on the bus at Oak Street. First we pass the school. Then the bus takes us over a bridge. Soon we see a tall building with a red flag. We pass lots of people walking. At Main Street, the bus driver stops the bus and Mom and I step off. Now it is time to shop!

 **Read each sentence.**
Circle T if it's true, or F if it's false.

We get on the bus on Oak Street.   T   F

The bus goes over the bridge first.   T   F

The tall building has a gold flag.   T   F

There are many people in the city.   T   F

We get off the bus at Main Street.   T   F

Recalling details in a story

Is That a Fact?

A **fact** is something you can prove. An **opinion** is what you feel or believe. You cannot prove it.

fact
Spot has brown eyes.

opinion
Spot has kind eyes.

 Circle the **fact** in each pair of sentences.

Baseball is fun.
A baseball team has nine players.

This rose is red.
Roses are pretty.

Dogs are good pets.
Dogs cannot climb trees.

Everyone likes ice cream.
This store sells ice cream.

This cap cost five dollars.
This cap looks good on me.

What's Your Opinion?

A fact can be proved. An opinion cannot be proved. It is what someone feels or believes.

 Decide if each sentence is a **fact** or an **opinion**. Circle **F** for **fact** or **O** for **opinion**.

Gina has curly hair.   **F**   **O**

 Turtles are ugly.   **F**   **O**

Summer is the best time of year.   **F**   **O**

The tree has green leaves.   **F**   **O**

 Cats make the best pets.   **F**   **O**

The home team won the game.   **F**   **O**

Discriminating between fact and opinion

Telling It All

Some sentences tell something. They are called **statements**. Every **statement** begins with a capital letter and ends with a **period**.

<u>T</u>he wind is blowing<u>.</u> ← period

 Circle the **statement** below.

Rain fell all day.

When will the rain stop?

 Fill in the ◯ by the **statement** that is written correctly.

◯ today is a cold day.
◯ Today is a cold day.

◯ The sky is blue.
◯ the sky is blue

◯ The children made a snowman
◯ The children made a snowman.

Recognizing statements and their usage of capital letters and periods

Did You Ask Me?

Some sentences ask something. They are called **questions.**
Every **question** begins with a capital letter and ends with a
question mark.

question mark

<u>W</u>hat is your phone number<u>?</u>

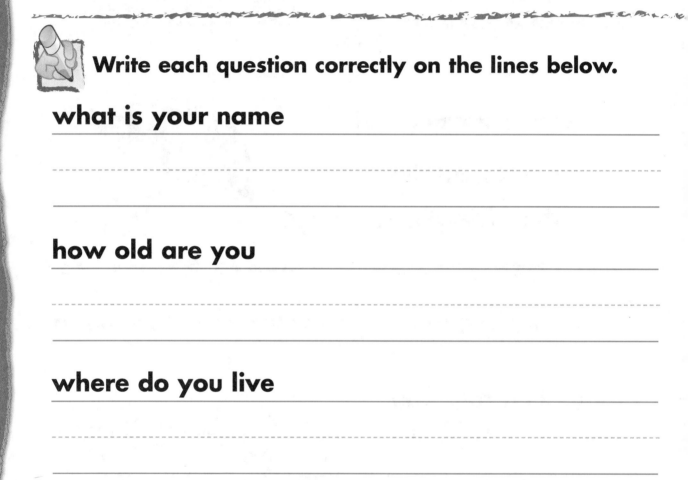

Write each question correctly on the lines below.

what is your name

how old are you

where do you live

 Circle the questions.

Where is my shoe?

Will you come with me?

The cat is in the tree.

Recognizing questions and their usage of capital letters and question marks

nice Ice

Every statement ends with a period.
Every question ends with a question mark.

 Add a period or a question mark to the end of each sentence below.

The day is cold but nice ____

Is the lake frozen ____

Mandy has new skates ____

Will Mandy learn a new trick ____

Jason can skate in circles ____

Who will win the race ____

At the Amusement Park

Write one statement and one question about the picture below.

Statement:

_____

_____

_____

Question:

_____

_____

_____

Writing statements and questions

Listening In

 Look at the picture.
The bird is asking a question.
The worm is answering.

What do you think the bird is asking?
Write its question on the lines.

Bird:

_____

_____

_____

_____

_____

What do you think the worm is saying?
Write its answer on the lines.

Worm:

_____

_____

_____

_____

Writing a dialogue

Jungle Questions

Circle the **10 question marks** hidden in this picture. Color the picture.

Visual discrimination

Month 8 Checklist

Hands-on activities to help your child in school!

GRAMMAR & PUNCTUATION

Kinds of Sentences: pages 227-228, 230
Subject-Verb Agreement: pages 231-234
Past Tense of Verbs: pages 235-240

Using verbs correctly is a complex skill that will take years to master. Worksheets for this month introduce some of the rules that everyone needs to be aware of in order to speak and write clearly.

❑ Complete the worksheets.
❑ Expose your child as often as possible to correct, standard English. Most books, for example, are written in standard English, while TV sitcoms frequently use nonstandard language. Rather than repeatedly point out differences between nonstandard and standard English, give your child enough chances to hear standard English so that using it will become natural and automatic.
❑ Make two paper puppets (or use two dolls) to represent a speaker who uses verbs correctly and another who makes errors. Using the poor-grammar puppet, make a statement with an error, such as "I does my work." Ask your child to use the good-grammar puppet to correct the error.

HANDWRITING

Friendly Letter: pages 241-242

Knowing where to write the parts of a friendly letter is as important as knowing how to write the message itself. Introduce your child to writing friendly letters with these activities:

❑ Complete the worksheets.
❑ Encourage your child to write a friendly letter to a relative or friend that he or she sees infrequently. Keep paper, envelope, and stamps at hand for a continued correspondence.

PHONICS & SPELLING

Vowels: pages 243-248

Your child has already been introduced to the most frequently used vowel sounds—the short and long vowel sounds. The phonics worksheets for this month introduce additional spelling patterns for selected long vowel sounds. Also, the worksheets introduce the long and short double *o* vowel sounds (the sounds in *goose* and *good*) that are represented by a variety of spellings.

❑ Complete the worksheets.
❑ Monitor your child's writing to find any words that he or she misspells regularly, particularly words with the spelling variations developed in this month's worksheets. Keep a list of these words, and in free time dictate a few to your child for him or her to spell aloud.

225

READING

Comprehension: pages 251-252
Sequence in Directions: pages 253-254

Help your child improve skills in understanding and following directions with these activities:

❑ Complete the worksheets.
❑ Make up hints for a household treasure hunt, in which your child reads a clue and follows the directions in it to find the next clue. The last clue directs the hunter to a small prize. Each hint should involve two or three steps. For example, a note might say, "Go to the hall closet. Look on the middle shelf. Turn over the gray hat."

VOCABULARY & WORD STUDY

Homonyms: pages 249-250

Many riddles and jokes, particularly puns, are based on homonyms, words that sound alike but have different spellings and meanings. Worksheets in this month will give your child further practice in recognizing homonyms and appreciating the humor they often provide.

❑ Complete the worksheets.
❑ Help your child make a collection of riddles that are based on homonyms, such as "What is black and white and red (read) all over?"
❑ Add words to the homonym memory game described in the Parent Checklist for Month 5, and play the game with your child.

COMPOSITION

Writing Exclamations and Commands: pages 229
Writing Directions: pages 255-256

In previous pages of this workbook, your child has read and followed multi-step directions. In this month, he or she has an opportunity to analyze a task and write directions for completing that task.

❑ Complete the worksheets.
❑ In a two-page composition activity for this month, your child is asked to write out the directions for a familiar task. Help your child prepare for this activity. While you do a job, discuss the steps you take as you do them. After you model this step-by-step description of your job, ask your child to talk about his or her job in the same orderly way.

Wow!

Some sentences show excitement. They are called **exclamations**. Every **exclamation** begins with a capital letter and ends with an **exclamation point**.

<u>W</u>atch out! ← exclamation point

 Circle the **exclamations** below.

I was so scared!

What time is it?

The ice cream truck is coming!

 Fill in the ○ by the **exclamation** that is written correctly.

○ This soup is hot!
○ this soup is hot

○ You are stepping on my toe?
○ You are stepping on my toe!

○ That is a pretty sunset!
○ that is a pretty sunset!

Recognizing exclamations and their usage of capital letters and exclamation points

Is That an Order?

Some sentences give directions or orders. They are called **commands**. Every **command** begins with a capital letter and ends with a period.

<u>P</u>ick a card<u>.</u> ← period

 Circle the **command** below.

Look at your card.

What card did you pick?

 Rewrite each **command** correctly.

turn off the light

_____

_____

make a wish

_____

_____

open the window

_____

_____

Recognizing commands and their usage of capital letters and periods

Winter Fun

Write one command and one exclamation about the picture.

Command:

_____

_____

_____

Exclamation:

_____

_____

_____

In the Lunch Room

 Add a period (.), a question mark (?), or an exclamation point (!) to each sentence below.

Wait in the lunch line ____

May I sit with you ____

Sam picked a fruit ____

I can't wait to eat ____

What would you like to eat ____

Get a plate for me, please ____

Pretty as a Picture

A verb usually ends in **s** when it tells about one person or thing. It usually does not end in **s** when it tells about more than one person or thing.

One bird sings.   **Many birds sing.**

 Read the first sentence in each pair and underline the verb. Rewrite the verb to fit the second sentence.

One ant crawls. Many ants _____.

Many ducks swim. One duck _____.

One bunny hops. Many bunnies _____.

Many flowers grow. One flower _____.

Choosing the correct form of verb to agree with the subject in number

Let's Go Shopping!

A verb usually ends in s when it tells about one person or thing. It usually does not end in s when it tells about more than one person or thing.

 Circle the verb that correctly completes each sentence.

Many people **come** / **comes** to the store.

The man **set** / **sets** food on the shelf.

Dad **chooses** / **choose** one box.

The cart **has** / **have** a squeaky wheel.

The clerks **press** / **presses** keys quickly.

Dad **take** / **takes** the bags to the car.

Choosing the correct form of a verb to agree with the subject in number

Has and Have

The verbs has and have are special. Use has after the words he, she or it, or with a noun.

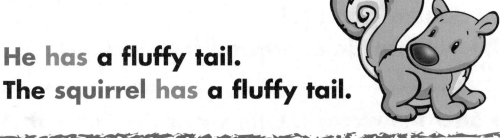

He has **a fluffy tail.**
The squirrel has **a fluffy tail.**

Use have after the words I, you, we or they, or with a plural noun.

They have **fluffy tails.**
Squirrels have **fluffy tails.**

"We have fluffy tails!"

has	have
he, she, it	I, you, we, they
noun	plural noun

 Fill in the ◯ by the sentence that is written correctly.

◯ **A dog has a tail.**
◯ **A dog have a tail.**

◯ I has **a nose.**
◯ I have **a nose.**

◯ We have **gum.**
◯ We has **gum.**

◯ Birds has **wings.**
◯ Birds have **wings.**

*Using **has** and **have**; present tense forms of the verb **to have***

Does and Do

The verbs does and do are special. Use does after the words he, she or it, or with a noun.

He **does** a good job.
The worker **does** a good job.

Use do after the words I, you, we or they, or with a plural noun.

They **do** a good job.
The workers **do** a good job.

"You **do** a good job!"

does	do
he, she, it	I, you, we, they
noun	plural noun

 Write does or do to complete each sentence.

Most people _____ their best.

She _____ good tricks.

I _____ my homework.

Jason _____ his chores.

*Using **does** and **do**; present tense forms of the verb **to do***

Talking about the Past

A verb can show that an action happened in the past.
Verbs that tell about the past often end in **ed**.

Zak kicked the ball.

Add **ed** to each verb to make it tell about the past.
Write the verb on the line.

Trina _____ to the park.
walk

Jim _____ a TV show.
watch

The baby _____ sleepy.
look

The worker _____ the board.
saw

The girls _____ a lot.
talk

*Forming past tense of regular verbs by adding **-ed***

Make That Double

Some verbs end in a single consonant after a single vowel. To make these verbs tell about the past, double the final consonant and add **ed.**

The final consonant in the word **hop** is **p.**

hop + p + ed = hopped

Now bunnies hop.
Yesterday bunnies hopped.

Rewrite each verb below so that it tells about the past. Remember to double the final consonant and add **ed.**

Now	In the Past
pet	_____
clap	_____

Use the verbs you wrote above to complete each sentence below.

Fans _____ for the winners.

Sue _____ her cat.

*Forming past tense of regular verbs by doubling final consonant before adding **-ed***

Move Out, Silent E!

Some verbs end in silent **e**. To make these verbs tell about the past, drop the silent **e** and add **ed**.

save + ed = sav**ed**
Tim **saved** string for two years.

 Rewrite each verb to make it tell about the past by dropping the silent **e** and adding **ed**.

The circus bears _____.
　　　　　　　　　　dance

Lia _____ she would win.
　　　hope

The painters _____ blue paint.
　　　　　　use

He _____ here last year.
　　move

We _____ a pie.
　　bake

Some Special Verbs

Some verbs end in y after a consonant. To make these verbs tell about the past, change the y to i and add ed.

Now workers **hurry**.

hur**r̶y̶** + ed = **hurried**

Yesterday workers **hurried**.

Make each verb tell about the past.
Change the y to i and add **ed**.

Now	In the Past
marry	
carry	
cry	

Use the verbs you wrote above to complete each sentence below.

Jill _____ Ted.

The baby _____ .

He _____ dishes.

A Puzzle about the Past

Read the clues.
Write the answers in the crossword puzzle.

ACROSS
2. The past of **carry**
5. The past of **sip**
6. The past of **play**

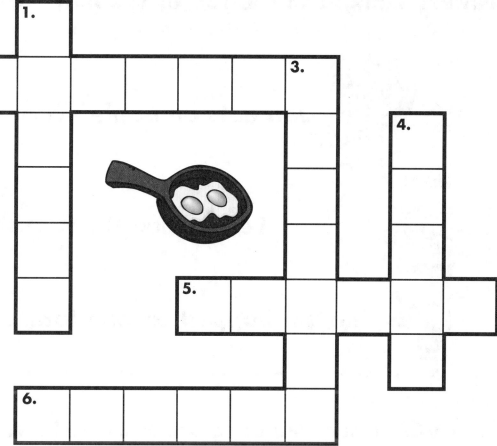

DOWN
1. The past of **talk**
3. The past of **drop**
4. The past of **fry**

Practice in forming past tense of verbs

239

now or In the Past?

 Circle the verbs that tell about the past.

The baby bear climbed a tree.

Hikers walked to the top of the hill.

Jan eats an apple every day.

Leo carried the flag.

The girl hopped on one foot.

Write a sentence using one of the verbs you circled above.

_____

_____

_____

_____

Recognizing verbs in past tense

Friend to Friend

 Read this letter.

May 11, 2003

Dear Linda,

Last week my family went to the zoo. The animals I liked the best were the monkeys. Here's a picture of one. Do you like monkeys, too?

Your friend,
Ally

 Circle the best answer.

Who wrote the letter?	**Linda**	**Ally**
Who got the letter?	**Ally**	**Linda**
When was it written?	**today**	**May 11, 2003**
What did it tell about?	**Linda**	**going to the zoo**

Writing a Friendly Letter

Write a letter to a friend. Write these things:
Line 1: today's date
Line 2: your friend's name
Lines 3, 4, and 5: your news
Line 6: your own name

(1) _____ , 200____

(2) **Dear** _____ ,

(3) _____

(4) _____

(5) _____

Your friend,

(6) _____

A Moose on the Moon

In some words, **oo** has the vowel sound you hear in **moon**.

m<u>oo</u>se

m<u>oo</u>n

f<u>oo</u>d

 Draw a line from each word to its matching picture.

boot

goose

noon

roof

tools

tooth

balloon

igloo

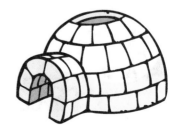

---

*Recognizing the long double **o** sound of **oo***

243

A Blue Crew on the Moon

Often, **ew** and **ue** have the same vowel sound as the **oo** in **moon**.

blue

crew

m**oo**n

 Choose the word that best completes each sentence and write it on the line.

When will the tulips _____ ?

| blew | bloom | blue |

Ron _____ a picture.

| drew | droop | due |

Mom put meat in the _____ .

| clue | gloom | stew |

Anna _____ the ball.

| true | threw | troop |

*Recognizing the long double **o** sound of **ew** and **ue***

Looking at oo

In some words, **oo** has the vowel sound you hear in **look**.

hood

look

brook

 Draw a line from each word to its matching picture.

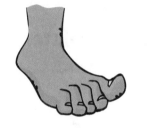

book

cookie

foot

hood

hook

wood

 Underline each word with the same vowel sound as **foot**.

We stood and took a good look at the

new school that was built out of wood.

Some Special Words

Read the words in the box below. They have the same vowel sound as look. Look at how the words are spelled.

could	would	bull
put	should	full

Choose one word from the box that best completes each sentence and write it on the line.

The box is _____ of pens.

I cannot reach that, but a tall person _____ .

A big _____ ran across the field.

You _____ always be polite.

If I had a dog, I _____ play with it.

I _____ the bike in the shed.

*Recognizing the short double **o** sound of **ou** and **u***

oo in Moon? Or oo in Look?

Read the words in the spaces below. If the word has the same vowel sound as moon, color the space *blue*. **If the word has the same vowel sound as look, color the space** *brown*. **If the space does not have a word, color it** *pink*.

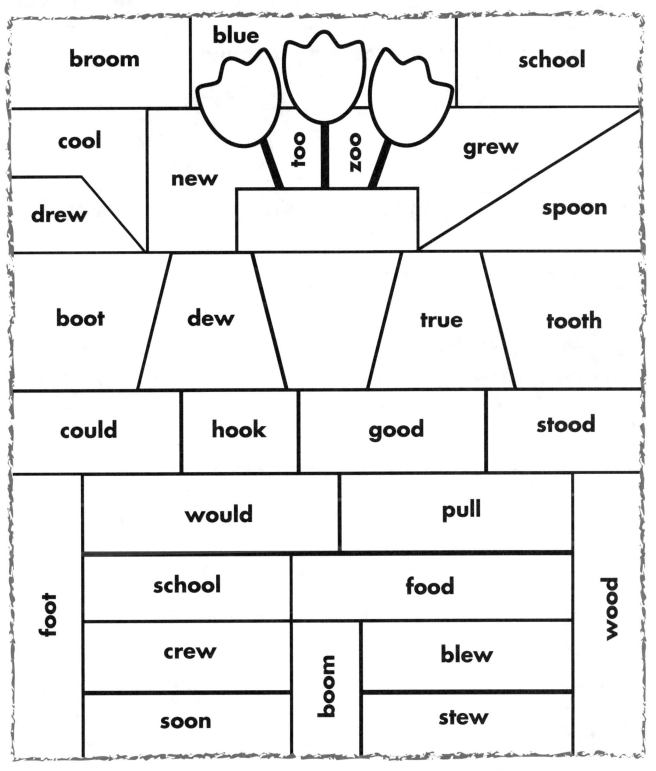

broom	blue	school
cool	new	grew
drew	too zoo	spoon
boot	dew	true tooth
could	hook	good stood
foot	would	pull wood
	school	food
	crew	boom blew
	soon	stew

Discriminating between the long and short double o vowel sounds

Surprising Spellings

In some words, ie has the long e sound.

chi<u>e</u>f　　　**f<u>ie</u>ld**　　　**bel<u>ie</u>ve**　　　**p<u>ie</u>ce**

In a few words, ei has the long a sound.

n<u>ei</u>ghbor　　　**<u>ei</u>ght**　　　**sl<u>ei</u>gh**　　　**w<u>ei</u>gh**

 Match each sentence with a picture.

The scale shows how much I weigh.

My neighbor lives next door to me.

Do you believe in fairies?

Flowers grow in that field.

*Recognizing irregular spellings of the **a** and **e** long vowel sounds*

Lots of Homonyms

Homonyms are words that sound alike but do not have the same spelling or meaning. Rose and rows are homonyms.

 Read the words in the box. Write each word underneath the picture of its homonym.

blew	pale	peek	plain
rows	stare	steel	way	weak

 steal

_____

 peak

_____

 blue

_____

 plane

_____

 week

_____

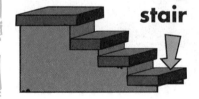 stair

_____

 pail

_____

 weigh

_____

 rose

_____

Hurray for Homonyms!

Each of these words has a homonym.

sew

bear

tail

pear

  Circle the word in each homonym pair that belongs in the sentence. Write it on the line.

 It is _____ hot outside!
           sew   **so**

The trees are _____ now.
           bare   **bear**

Tell us the funny _____ again.
           tail   **tale**

I have a new _____ of shoes.
           pear   **pair**

Recognizing and writing homonyms

Make a Silly Riddle Book

 Read and follow these directions to make a little book of riddles.

1. **First tear this page out of the book and turn in over.**

2. **Next, fold the page along the line of ✶✶✶✶✶✶✶. Make sure the line is on the outside.**

3. **Next, fold the page along the line of •••••. Be sure the book title is on the outside.**

4. **Write your name on the line on the front cover.**

Silly Riddles

This book belongs to:

Do not make a move. I have you covered.

3

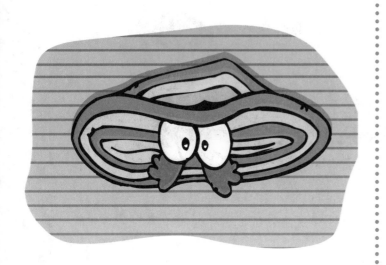

What did the rug say
to the floor?

What did the duck eat
with her soup?

Why is the elephant
always late?

He takes a long time to pack his trunk.

Silly Riddles

This book belongs to:

_____

Time for Lunch

When you give directions, tell about the steps in order.

Read these directions. Number the steps in order from 1 to 4.

It is easy to make a cheese sandwich. First spread butter on two slices of bread. Next put some cheese between the bread slices. Cut the sandwich in half. Now it is ready to eat!

Understanding sequence in directions

Making a Cool Drink

  Read each step in these directions. Draw a line between each step and its picture. Number the steps in order from 1 to 6.

_____ **Get out a pitcher.**

_____ **Mix the water and the powder.**

_____ **Pour water into the pitcher.**

_____ **Take a drink!**

_____ **Pour drink powder into the water.**

_____ **Pour the drink into a glass.**

Understanding sequence in directions

A Four-Step Job

Think of a small job that you can do in only four steps. Think of each of the steps you follow to do that job.

 **Write the name of the job. In the boxes below, draw pictures of the four steps in order.**

My job is _____

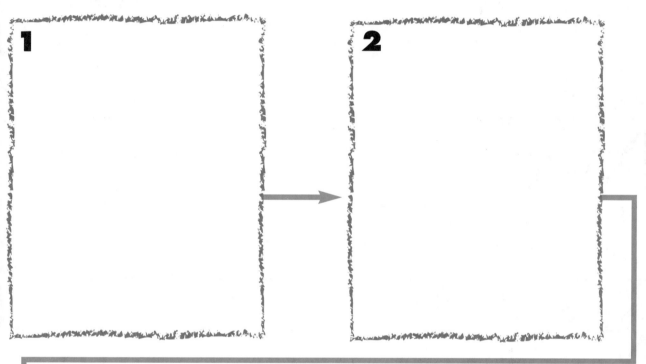

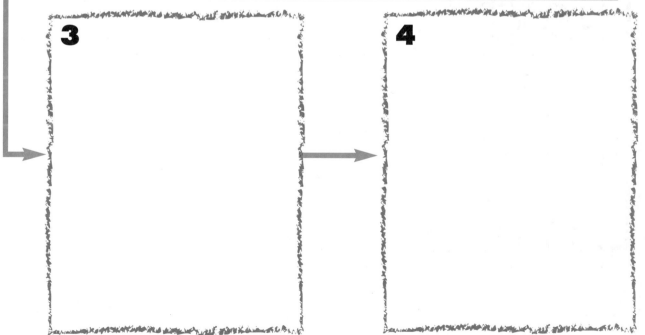

Using a graphic organizer for planning a set of directions

How to . . .

 You have made pictures of the four steps it takes to do the job you chose. Now write the words for the directions.

Step 1

First

Step 2

Next

Step 3

Next

Step 4

Last

Writing directions for completing a simple task

Month 9 Checklist

Hands-on activities to help your child in school!

PHONICS & SPELLING

Vowel Sounds (Diphthongs): pages 259-261

A diphthong is a vowel sound represented by two letters. In Month 8, *ei* as in *eight* and *ew* as in *crew* were introduced. In this month's phonics worksheets, your child will become familiar with certain spelling patterns that represent other diphthongs.

❑ Complete the worksheets.
❑ Write the diphthong OI and its alternate spelling OY on one index card, and the diphthong OU and its alternate spelling OW on another card. Hold up the cards one at a time and have your child name a word with each diphthong sound. Ask which of the two spellings of the sound each word uses.

READING

Reading Comprehension: 283-284
Reading for Detail: pages 262, 279-280
Main Idea: pages 277-278

This month's worksheets develop essential reading skills introduced in earlier months.

❑ Complete the worksheets.
❑ At an art museum, visit galleries with realistic paintings. Invite your child to identify the main idea or situation that each artist is trying to represent. Then ask your child to list two or three details about the painting that support that main idea.
❑ Ask your child to read aloud a paragraph of an easy-to-read book or an entire page of a picture book. Help him or her restate the main idea of the passage.

VOCABULARY & WORD STUDY

Homonyms: pages 263-264
Synonyms: pages 273-274
Compound Words: pages 281-282

Knowing the precise meanings of many words will help your child excel not only in reading but also in speaking and writing. This month's vocabulary worksheets focus on three types of words, introducing two of them. Synonyms are words that mean the same thing, or almost the same thing, such as *easy* and *simple*. A compound word is made up of two smaller words, such as *freeway*.

❑ Complete the worksheets.
❑ Celebrate a "Synonym Day" with your child. Post a sheet of paper in the house and record synonym pairs that your child uses (or recognizes in others' speech) during the day. At the end of the day, read the list with your child.
❑ Have your child scan a newspaper article and circle every compound word he or she finds.

GRAMMAR & PUNCTUATION

Pronouns: pages 265-268
Past Tense of Verbs: pages 269-272

This month's grammar worksheets introduce the concept of the pronoun—a word that stands for a noun. They also continue to develop the rules regarding the use of verbs.

❑ Complete the worksheets.
❑ Continue to use the puppets (or dolls) that were suggested in the grammar activities for Month 8. This time, have the bad-grammar puppet use pronouns incorrectly or use the wrong verb form to show past tense. The good-grammar puppet should correct the other puppet's errors.
❑ Start a word jar. Select different shades of construction paper for the different parts of speech that your child is learning—for example, blue for nouns, red for verbs, and green for pronouns. (Later you will add two more shades for adjectives and adverbs.) Cut the sheets of construction paper into word-size slips of paper and write words of your choice on them. Each day have your child select one or more slips from the jar and dictate (or write) a sentence using the chosen word(s).

HANDWRITING

Thank-You Note: pages 275-276
Cursive Alphabet: pages 285-288

In many school districts, cursive writing is introduced in the second half of the second grade. Give your child practice in recognizing and writing cursive letters with these activities:

❑ Complete the worksheets.
❑ Make four sets of cards for a memory game. On one set, print all the capital letters; on another, write the capital letters in cursive. On a third set, print all the lowercase letters; on the fourth, write the lowercase letters in cursive. Then select five to ten capital letters, in both printed and cursive forms, and use those cards in a memory game. Lay the cards face down in random order. Take turns turning two cards over. If a player's chosen cards show matching printed and cursive forms of the same letter, that player keeps the cards and takes another turn. If they show different letters, the next player takes a turn. Gradually expand the game to include all the letter pairs, both capital and lowercase.
❑ Have your child apply his or her letter-writing skills by writing a thank-you note as soon as possible after receiving a gift.

The Joyful Noise of oi and oy!

Both oi and oy have the same vowel sound.

b**oy**

b**oi**l

 Underline oi or oy in each word.

oil	choice	noise	point
join	annoy	toy	joy

 **Read each sentence. Rewrite the oi word and the oy word on the lines below.**

The boy will boil a hot dog.

_____   _____

An oyster is not noisy.

_____   _____

Point to the cowboy.

_____   _____

Recognizing the diphthongs oi and oy

And Now About ow and ou

Both ow and ou can stand for the same vowel sound.

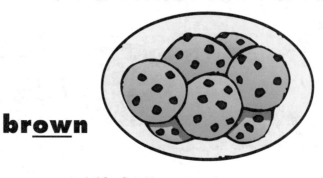

br<u>ow</u>n   **r<u>ou</u>nd**

 Underline ow or ou in each word.

how   **about**   **loud**   **flower**

cowboy   **house**   **down**   **mouth**   **found**

 **Read each sentence. Rewrite the ou word and the ow word on the lines below.**

The clown likes to laugh and shout.

_____   _____

The cowboy found a daisy.

_____   _____

Now we will sit on the ground.

_____   _____

Recognizing the diphthongs ow and ou

Ought We to Trust ou?

ou takes different sounds. Say each word below and listen for the **ou** sound.

| c**ou**ld | c**ou**ch | c**ou**gh |

When **ou** is followed by **ght** the **gh** is silent and only the **t** is heard at the end of the word.

She **b<u>ou</u>ght** a pair of skates.

 Each sentence has one **ou** word in it. Circle the red word below the sentence that has the same **ou** sound.

We **ought** to wear coats.

| about | thought |

When **should** we come in?

| bought | would |

We are going **out** to play.

| found | should |

I **would** like to jump rope.

| mouth | could |

James **found** a ball.

| mouth | cough |

A Proud Day

 Read Joy's story.

Our family went to town to see the parade. About noon we joined a big crowd. My brother Roy was in the band. Dad pointed out where he was. We could all see him and we shouted and waved. The band music sounded good and loud.

The parade lasted about half an hour. We all enjoyed it. If I had my choice, I would see a parade every day.

 Write the answers to these questions about the story.

Where did Joy go to see the parade?

_____

_____

What did Joy's family do when they saw Roy?

_____

_____

What did Joy have to say about the band music?

_____

_____

Reading for detail

Mixed-up Homonyms

Homonyms are words that sound the same but have different meanings and spellings.

 Choose a homonym to complete each sentence and write it on the line.

This _____ is strong.

not	knot

I do _____ see my friends.

I need to _____ a letter.

mail	male

Champ is a _____ kitten.

Spot is _____ pet.

our	hour

The bus comes every _____.

Do you want _____ more?

some	sum

The _____ of 1 plus 1 is 2.

Using homonyms correctly

Homonym Word Search

Find and circle each word in these homonym pairs.

beet beat
flower flour
know no
rap wrap
whale wail

creek creak
whole hole
made maid
real reel
wood would

w	z	a	m	a	m	a	d	e	h	r	b
r	l	r	f	n	w	h	o	l	e
a	n	t	l	o	o	c	l	n	e
p	f	l	o	w	e	r	e	x	k
r	w	o	u	l	d	e	m	w	j
e	b	d	r	a	p	a	a	w	a
a	h	c	r	e	e	k	i	h	b
l	b	e	a	w	o	o	d	a	e
p	k	n	o	w	w	a	i	l	a
r	e	e	l	r	s	b	e	e	t

Recognizing homonyms

I Am Talking about Me

If you want to talk about yourself, you could use your name. Or you could use the **pronouns** I or me. **Pronouns** are words that take the place of other nouns.

Use the **pronoun** I in the subject of a sentence. The subject tells **who** or **what** does something.

I went to school.

My pet came with me.

Use the **pronoun** me in the predicate of a sentence. The predicate tells what the person or thing **does**.

 Circle the correct **pronoun** to complete each sentence.

 have a pet hamster.

When I call, he comes to .

 named my hamster Porky.

Porky likes .

Recognizing and understanding pronouns

We Are Talking about Us

Words that take the place of nouns are called **pronouns**. **We** and **us** are **pronouns**.

Use **we** in the subject of a sentence.
We had a picnic.

Use **us** in the predicate.
Friends came with **us**.

 Fill in the ○ by each sentence that uses **we** and **us** correctly.

○ We played games.
○ Us played games.

○ Mom drove **us** home.
○ Mom drove **we** home.

○ Brad showed **we** a new game.
○ Brad showed **us** a new game.

○ Us ate some good food.
○ We ate some good food.

Recognizing and understanding pronouns

My Picture

Pronouns are words that take the place of nouns. Use the **pronouns** he, she, and they in the subject of a sentence.

He batted first.
She batted next.
They both got hits.

Use the **pronouns** him, her, and them in the predicate of a sentence.

Kay threw the ball to him.
He threw it back to her.
The fans cheered for them.

 Circle the correct **pronoun** to complete each sentence.

The coach gave them / they a smile.

Him / He likes baseball.

Laura tries hard for him / he .

The fans gave she / her a hand.

They / Them had fun.

Searching for Pronouns

 Circle one **pronoun** in each sentence.

I am the winner!

The fairy gave him three wishes.

They came to the party.

She skates fast.

Mom read a story to me.

The clown did a trick for us.

Recognizing pronouns in sentences

Was and Were

Some verbs change in special ways to tell about the past.
See how **is**, **are**, and **am** change.

Now	In the Past
I **am**	I **was**
you **are**	you **were**
he, she, or it **is**	he, she, or it **was**
we **are**	we **were**
they **are**	they **were**

Write **was** or **were** to complete each sentence.

I _____ up in the tree.

They _____ in the park.

She _____ cold.

You _____ on the phone.

*Using **was** and **were**; past tense forms of the verb **to be***

You Were Right!

 Fill in the ◯ by the sentence that uses **was** or **were** correctly.

◯ He was on the way home.
◯ He were on the way home.

◯ You were the first in line.
◯ You was the first in line.

◯ She were happy with the gift.
◯ She was happy with the gift.

◯ It was my fault.
◯ It were my fault.

◯ They was on my team.
◯ They were on my team.

Yesterday and Today

Some verbs change in special ways to tell about the past.

Now	In the Past
has, have does, do	had did

 Draw a line to connect each sentence with the verb that completes it.

have   Yesterday I _____ a fever.

had   Today I _____ a cough.

do   Today farmers _____ hard jobs.

did   Long ago, farmers _____ even harder jobs.

did   Yesterday Waldo _____ a silly trick.

does   Now he _____ a better trick.

has   Yesterday Misty _____ no kittens.

had   Now Misty _____ three kittens.

*Using **had** and **did**; past tense forms of the verbs **to have** and **to do***

Crack the Code!

 Change each word in ( ) to tell about the past. Write each letter of the word on a line space. Some line spaces have a number below them that you will use to solve a riddle.

You (want) ___ ___ ___ ___ ___ ___ ice cream.
　　　　　　　 1

I (spy) ___ ___ ___ ___ ___ a robin yesterday.
　　　 2

You (have) ___ ___ ___ a good idea.
　　　　　　 3

The birds (are) ___ ___ ___ ___ loud yesterday.
　　　　　 4　　 **5**

Jess (look) ___ ___ ___ ___ ___ ___ at the sunset.
　　　　　 6　　 **7**

 Solve the riddle using the numbered letters.

Why did the hummingbird hum?

It did not ___ ___ ___ ___ the ___ ___ ___ ___ ___ .
　　　　 7 **1** **6** **4** 　　 **4** **6** **5** **3** **2**

Past tense verb review

Synonyms to Know

Words with the same or almost the same meaning are called **synonyms**.

Close and **shut** are **synonyms**.

 Draw a line between each word and its **synonym**.

little	**sound**
make	**small**
noise	**after**
behind	**build**

 Write the **synonym** for each word on the line.

small _____   **build** _____

behind _____   **noise** _____

More Synonyms to Know

Words with the same or almost the same meaning are called synonyms.

Start and **begin** are **synonyms.**

 Draw a line between each word and its synonym.

big	**grab**
yell	**town**
take	**shout**
city	**large**

 Write the synonym for each word on the line.

yell _____   grab _____

city _____   large _____

Many Thanks!

Read this thank-you note. Look at the names of the different parts of the note. Then follow the directions below.

Date	June 22, 2003
Greeting	Dear Aunt Lisa,
Body	Thank you for the shirt you sent me for my birthday. It fits fine. I like it a lot.
Closing	Your nephew, Jerry

Circle each comma (,) in the note. Now circle the word that tells where each comma is.

The comma in the date comes after the ___ .

month	day	year

The comma in the greeting comes after ___ .

Dear	Aunt	Lisa

The comma in the closing comes after ___ .

Your	favorite	nephew

Writing a Thank-You Note

Write a thank-you note to a friend. Fill in the lines. Remember to use commas correctly.

Line 1: today's date
Line 2: your friend's name
Lines 3, 4, and 5: Tell what nice thing your friend did.
Line 6: your own name

(1) _____

(2) **Dear** _____ **,**

(3) _____

(4) _____

(5) _____

Your friend,

(6) _____

276

What's the Main Idea?

The main idea is the most important idea.

 Underline the main idea of each picture.

The giant is friendly.

The giant scares people.

The clown is sad.

The clown is funny.

There is plenty to eat.

There is nothing to eat.

A new family moved in.

My friend moved away.

Identifying main ideas

Looking for the Main Idea

The main idea is the most important idea in a paragraph.

 **Read each paragraph, then fill in the ○ next to the main idea.**

Trees are useful plants. Trees clean the air around us. On a hot day, they give us shade. We can use their wood to build our homes. Trees also make the world pretty.

○ **Trees make us clean.**

○ **Trees are pretty.**

○ **Trees are useful.**

Joey had a good day. He found a dime on the ground. He got an A on his work. A friend chose him for her team. His mom gave him a big hug.

○ **Joey has lots of friends.**

○ **Joey had a good day.**

○ **Joey is rich.**

Reading for main idea

Details, Details

Details are facts that tell more about the main idea.

 **Look for details as you read this paragraph.**

> My cat, Tiger, is my best friend. He has orange and white stripes. His eyes are green. At night he sleeps at the foot of my bed. He wakes me up by purring in my ear.

 Circle the answer to each question.

What is the name of the cat?

| Tiger | Kitty |

What colors are the stripes on the cat?

| white and black | orange and white |

What color are his eyes?

| blue | green |

Where does the cat sleep?

| on the pillow | at the foot of the bed |

A Backyard Picnic

Details tell more about the main idea.

 Look for **details** as you read this story.

Last night our family had a picnic in our yard. We ate hot dogs, cheese, and fruit. We played hide-and-seek. When it got dark, we went inside. I love picnics!

 Write the answer to each question.

Where was the picnic?

_____

What did the family eat?

_____

What game did they play?

_____

What happened when it got dark?

_____

Reading for detail

One Word from Two

A compound word is made of two smaller words.

tug + boat = **tugboat**

 Find and write two words in each **compound word.**

_____ + _____ = sunshine

_____ + _____ = sailboat

_____ + _____ = seashell

_____ + _____ = starfish

_____ + _____ = swimsuit

Recognizing compound words

Putting Words Together

A compound word is made of two smaller words.

black + bird = **blackbird**

Write a **compound word** by putting each pair of words together.

cook + book = _____

pan + cake = _____

blue + berry = _____

grape + fruit = _____

high + chair = _____

Forming compound words

if a woodchuck
could chuck wood.

How much wood would
a woodchuck chuck,

if a woodchuck
could chuck wood?

He'd chuck all the wood
that a woodchuck could . . .

Cursive Matchup, Part 1

 Look at the letters below.
The blue letters are shown in cursive writing.

a b c d e f g h i j k l

a b c d e f g h i j k l

 Trace each cursive letter.

a

b

c

d

e

f

g

h

i

j

k

l

Cursive Matchup, Part II

Look at the letters below.
The blue letters are shown in cursive writing.

m n o p q r s t u v w x y z

m n o p q r s t u v w x y z

Trace each cursive letter.

m

n

o

p

q

r

s

t

u

v

w

x

y

z

Recognizing and tracing lowercase letters in cursive

Matching Capital in Cursive 1

 Look at the letters below.
The blue letters are shown in cursive writing.

$\mathcal{A}\ \mathcal{B}\ \mathcal{C}\ \mathcal{D}\ \mathcal{E}\ \mathcal{F}\ \mathcal{G}\ \mathcal{H}\ \mathcal{I}\ \mathcal{J}\ \mathcal{K}\ \mathcal{L}$

A B C D E F G H I J K L

 Match.

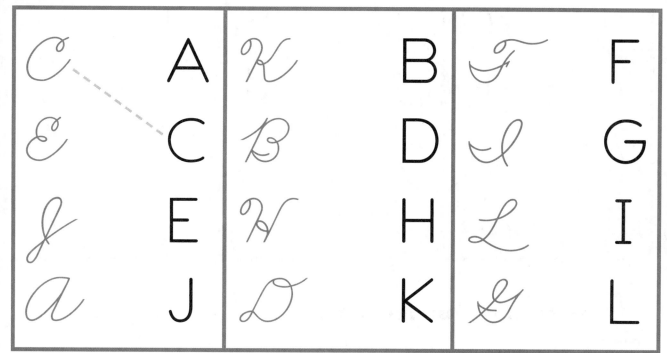

 Trace these cursive letters.

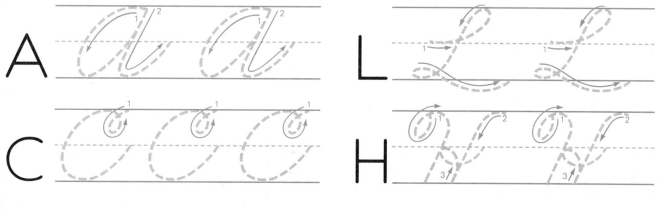

Matching Capitals in Cursive II

 Look at the letters below.
The blue letters are shown in cursive writing.

M N O P Q R S T U V W X Y Z

M N O P Q R S T U V W X Y Z

O	M	*P*	N	*U*	Q
R	O	*n*	P	*X*	U
m	R	*T*	S	*W*	W
V	V	*y*	T	*Q*	X
Z	Z	*S*	Y		

 Trace these cursive letters.

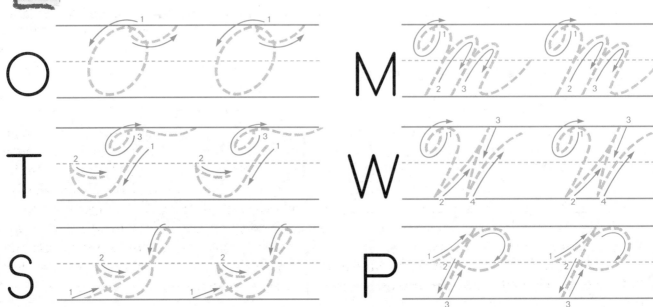

O   M

T   W

S   P

Recognizing and tracing capital letters in cursive

Month 10 Checklist

Hands-on activities to help your child in school!

PHONICS & SPELLING

Silent Letters: pages 291-294

Your child may already recognize several words with silent letters, such as *write*, *comb*, and *know*. Phonics worksheets for this month focus attention on particular spelling patterns that include letters that are not heard. Help your child recognize and spell words with silent letters with these activities:

❑ Complete the worksheets.
❑ Devote a week to creating a "Tricky Word List." Over the first six days, have your child write on a separate slip of paper each word he or she comes across that has a silent letter. Provide a folder for storing the papers. At the end of the week, help your child alphabetize the words. Then have him or her write the words in order in a notebook, illustrating as many of the words as possible.

GRAMMAR & PUNCTUATION

Past Tense of Irregular Verbs: pages 295, 297, 299
Adjectives: pages 301-306
Adverbs: pages 313-314

One of the concepts introduced in this month's grammar worksheets is the irregular verb—a verb that changes form in ways that do not follow the regular rules. This workbook touches on only a few of the many irregular verbs in English. Clearly, you cannot expect your child to master this concept in a single year. Throughout your child's schooling, this and other grammar concepts will be revisited every year in greater depth. Helping your child become familiar with the terms and rules will lay a foundation for future success in both oral and written language.

❑ Complete the worksheets.
❑ Have your child add a second part to the "Tricky Word List" suggested in the Phonics & Spelling activities above. As before, spend a week collecting and recording irregular verbs. This time, make sure your child notes on each slip both the present and past tense forms of each verb, such as *give* and *gave*. On the last day of the week, help your child alphabetize the words. Then have your child add a Part Two to the notebook, recording and illustrating the verbs.
❑ After your child has completed the worksheets on adjectives, add adjectives written on a fourth shade of construction paper to your word jar. (See the Month 9 Checklist.) After completing the adverb worksheets, add adverbs written on a fifth shade. Encourage your child to select two slips of different colors and use both words in a single sentence.

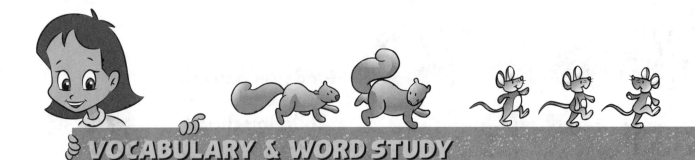

VOCABULARY & WORD STUDY

Synonyms: pages 307-308

Help your child develop an appreciation for synonyms with these activities:

❑ Complete the worksheets.
❑ Demonstrate the life-long importance of synonyms by showing your child a thesaurus (preferably one written for children) and, together, look up synonyms for a word or two. If you use a word-processing program, show how the program provides synonyms for selected words.

READING

Comprehension: pages 296, 298, 300, 315-316
Cause and Effect: pages 309-310
Predicting Outcomes: pages 311-312

Being aware of cause and effect helps your child make connections between events in a story or explanation. Predicting outcomes focuses a reader's attention on the important elements in a story or explanation. Help your child develop these essential reading skills with the following activities:

❑ Complete the worksheets.
❑ Discuss with your child the causes and effects in simple nursery rhymes, such as "Little Miss Muffet." Say, "Why did Miss Muffet run away?" Sing fun songs such as "I Know an Old Lady Who Swallowed a Fly" and "The House That Jack Built" that develop chains of cause and effect.
❑ As you read aloud to your child, stop at critical points in the story. Ask, "What do you think will happen now? Why do you think so?" As needed, point out clues that he or she may have missed. Then read on to find out how accurate the prediction was.

COMPOSITION

Planning and Writing a Description: pages 317-318

In the composition activity for this month, your child applies what was taught earlier in the grammar worksheets about adjectives and adverbs.

❑ Complete the worksheets.
❑ In this month's composition activity, your child is asked to describe a toy. Help your child prepare for this activity by encouraging him or her to describe other items around the house, such as items of clothing, foods, or pets. If your child leaves out important details, ask leading questions to help him or her provide a more complete verbal picture of the item.

Silent Letters I

In words beginning with **wr**, the **w** is silent and only the **r** is heard.

write

wren

 Underline the silent letter in each word below, then draw a line to match each word with its picture.

wrap

wring

wrist

 Write the missing word in each sentence using the words in the box.

| wren   wrong   wrap |

A _____ sings a pretty song.

He knows right from _____ .

She will _____ the gift.

Silent Letters II

In words beginning with **kn** or **gn**, the **k** or **g** is silent and only the **n** in heard.

 **kn**ee

 **gn**aw

 Underline the silent letter in each word below, then draw a line to match each word with its picture.

gnu

knock

knot

 Write the missing word in each sentence using the words in the box.

| gnu | knee | knock |

We saw a _____ at the zoo.

When I fell, I cut my _____ .

He heard a _____ at the door.

292

*Recognizing silent **k** in **kn** and silent **g** in **gn***

Silent Letters III

In words ending with **mb**, the **b** is usually silent.

la<u>mb</u>   **co<u>mb</u>**

In a few words beginning with **h**, the **h** is silent.

<u>h</u>our   **<u>h</u>onest**

 Read the two words in each box and underline the silent letters. Circle the correct word to complete each sentence.

Your hand has one ___.

crumb   thumb

The show is one ___ long.

hour   herb

Let's ___ that hill.

crumb   climb

Do not lie. Be ___.

honest   honor

The bird rests on a tree ___.

lamb   limb

*Recognizing silent **b** in **mb** and silent **h** in certain words*

Silent Letter Crossword Puzzle

Some of the words in the box are puzzle answers.

Fill in the puzzle using the words in the box to help you.

climb	herb	knot	thumb
crumb	hour	new	wrench
gnome	knew	not	wring
gnu	knife	ring	wrong

ACROSS

1. not right
3. sounds like **knot**
6. to go up
7. plant used in cooking

DOWN

1. a tool
2. an animal
4. on your hand but not a finger
5. a thing that cuts

Not Just Ordinary Verbs

Some verbs change in special ways to tell about the past.

Now	In the Past
come, comes	came
say, says	said
sit, sits	sat
write, writes	wrote

Rewrite the verb shown below each line so it tells about the past.

Fans _____ to the ball park.
come

Kris _____ the magic word.
says

The cat _____ by the fire.
sits

Steve was sick Yesterday

Mom _____ a note to my teacher.
writes

Forming the past tense of irregular verbs

295

Rhymes from Long Ago

 Read these old nursery rhymes and circle all the verbs that tell about the past.

Little Jack Horner sat in a corner
Eating a tasty pie.
He put in his thumb and pulled out a plum
And said, "What a good boy am I!"

Little Miss Muffet sat on a tuffet
Eating her curds and whey.
Along came a spider and sat down beside her
And frightened Miss Muffet away.

 Answer these questions.

1. How many verbs did you circle? _____

2. How many of these verbs
   were formed by adding **ed**? _____

3. How many were formed in special ways? _____

Reading; identifying past tense verbs

Let's Talk About the Past!

Some verbs change in special ways to tell about the past.

Now	In the Past
begin, begins	began
lose, loses	lost
run, runs	ran
see, sees	saw

Fill in the ○ beside the sentence that tells about the past correctly.

○ The workers begin the job last week.
○ The workers began the job last week.

○ Yesterday I lost my glove.
○ Yesterday I lose my glove.

○ Two squirrels run by me a minute ago.
○ Two squirrels ran by me a minute ago.

○ Last night I saw a shooting star.
○ Last night I see a shooting star.

Forming the past tense of irregular verbs

297

A Story in the Past

 **Read the story and circle all the verbs that tell about the past.**

Peter had two dogs named Flip and Flop.

Flip was very good. If Peter said, "Come here, Flip," Flip came. If Peter said, "Sit, Flip," Flip sat.

Flop was not as good. If Peter said, "Come here, Flop," Flop ran away! If Peter said, "Sit, Flop," Flop never sat.

One day, Flip was sick. He had to go to the vet. Peter was sad. He cried. Flop was sad, too. Peter needed a friend.

"Come here, Flop," he said. Flop came! "Sit next to me," said Peter. Flop sat! He licked Peter on the hand and stayed with him a long time.

After that, Flop always listened to Peter. When Flip got better and came home, Peter smiled and said, "Now I have the two best dogs in the world!"

 Write a sentence using one of the verbs you circled.

_____

_____

Then and Now

Some verbs change in special ways to tell about the past.

Now	In the Past
break, breaks	broke
eat, eats	ate
fall, falls	fell
go, goes	went

 Circle the verb that completes each sentence correctly.

Snow **falls** / **fell** last night.

Last week the boys **break** / **broke** a fancy vase.

Last summer we **go** / **went** on a long trip.

When I was little, I **ate** / **eat** baby food.

More Rhymes from the Past

 Read these old nursery rhymes and circle all the verbs that tell about the past.

Jack and Jill went up the hill
To fetch a pail of water.
Jack fell down and broke his crown,
And Jill came tumbling after.

Mary had a little lamb.
Its fleece was white as snow.
And everywhere that Mary went
The lamb was sure to go.

 Write a sentence using one of the verbs you circled.

_____

_____

Reading; identifying verbs in the past tense

Words That Describe

Some words tell more about nouns. These words are called **adjectives**. **Adjectives** can answer these questions:

What kind?
fuzzy bears

How many?
two bears

What color?
brown bears

  Underline the **adjective** used in the first sentence, then circle the **adjective** that completes the second sentence.

This is a pretty flower.

This is a _____ flower.
    read   red

I see tiny mice.

I see _____ mice.
   throw   three

She has red hair.

She has _____ hair.
   long   smile

The bus is big.

The bus is _____ .
   drive   yellow

Recognizing adjectives

In the Summertime

Adjectives are words that tell more about nouns.

Write an **adjective** from the box to complete each sentence.

lazy	brown	white	two

A _____ bird sings.
What color?

The clouds are _____.
What color?

Can you see _____ squirrels?
How many?

A _____ dog sleeps under a tree.
What kind?

Choosing adjectives to complete sentences

The Great Adjective Search

Adjectives tell more about nouns. Some **adjectives** answer these questions: **What kind? How many? What color?**

 Circle two **adjectives** in each sentence.

Red fish swim beside green seaweed.

One clam sits on the tan sand.

Nosy eels look into the old ship.

Can you see the gold coins in the open chest?

Three happy seahorses play by the ship.

Surprises wait under the cool, blue sea.

Identifying adjectives in sentences

My Picture

Circle the **adjectives** in the box.
Cross out the other words.

four	green	peas	proud
rake	red	two	works

Write an **adjective** from the box to complete
each sentence.

Mike is _____ of his garden.

It has _____ scarecrows.

Mike picked _____ carrots.

He likes _____ beans.

The flowers are pink and _____.

Identifying and using adjectives

Rhyming Fun

Write an **adjective** from the box to make a
two-word rhyme for each picture.

big	**brown**	**fat**	**green**
new	**one**	**red**	**ten**

red _____
sled

_____
sun

_____
men

_____
cat

_____
clown

_____
shoe

_____
pig

_____
queen

Crossword Puzzle Fun

 Fill in this crossword puzzle. The answer to every clue is an **adjective**.

ACROSS

5. **The color of the sun**
6. **The number of noses you have**
8. **The number of toes you have**
9. **Not dry, but ____**

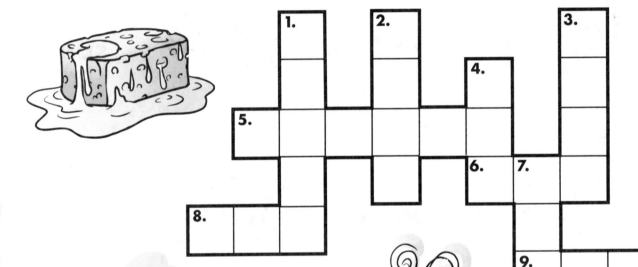

DOWN

1. **The color of grass**
2. **Not hot but ____**
3. **The color of the sky**
4. **The number of eyes she has**
7. **The opposite of old**

Adjective review

Searching for Synonyms

Synonyms are words with the same or nearly the same meaning. **Go** and **leave** are synonyms.

 Draw a line between each word and its synonym.

see   tale

below   under

picture   look

story   photo

 Write the synonym for each word.

below _____   look _____

story _____   photo _____

Synonyms? Certainly!

Synonyms are words with the same or nearly the same meaning.

Draw a line between each word and its synonym.

car   earth

world   correct

right   auto

night   evening

Write the synonym for each word.

car _____   evening _____

right _____   earth _____

Why Did This Happen?

The cause is the reason why something happens.
The effect is what happens.

Cause
Jenny gave her flower water.

Effect
The flower grew tall and strong.

Draw a line to connect each **cause** with its **effect**.

CAUSE

 Bear was hungry.

 Bear was tired.

 Bear sat in the sun.

 Bear went far away.

EFFECT

 He got a sunburn.

 He ate a big meal.

 He got lost.

 He went to bed.

Be a Detective!

Good detectives know that there is a reason for everything that happens. The reason is the cause. What happens is the effect.

 Use clues in the picture to discover causes and effects. Draw a line between each effect and its cause.

EFFECT	CAUSE
The boy runs away.	**She is tired.**
The girl is angry.	**He got a nice gift.**
The baby is yawning.	**She fell into the water**
Dad is smiling.	**Bees chase him.**

Understanding cause and effect

What Comes Next?

It is fun to guess what will happen next in stories.
Another name for guessing is **predicting**. To **predict** well,
you must pay attention to story clues.

 These pictures tell part of a story. Use the story clues
below to **predict** what will happen next.

 Draw a picture of what you **predicted**.

What Happened Next?

 Read this part of a story.

Long ago, fairies had special powers.

One day a fairy came into a toy shop. She touched a toy dog. The dog became a real dog. She touched a toy horse. The horse became real, too. Last she touched a puppet that looked like a boy.

 Draw a picture of what you predict will happen next.

Predicting outcomes

Tell Me More!

Adverbs tell how an action is done.

The hare ran <u>fast</u>.

 Write an adverb from the box to complete each sentence.

| brightly | fast | loudly | quietly | slowly |

The fire engine blew its horn _____ .

The old man walked _____ .

In the library, we talk _____ .

The sun shines _____ .

Race horses run _____ .

Interesting Details

Adverbs tell how an action is done. Many **adverbs** are formed by adding **ly** at the end of an **adjective**.

nice + ly = **nicely.**

She sang nicely.

 Change each **adjective** below into an **adverb** by adding **ly** at the end of the word. Write the **adverb** on the line.

 **The bunny hopped** _____.

quick

 **This bus drives** _____.

smooth

 **The bear danced** _____.

bad

The dog barked _____.

loud

 **The boat sailed** _____.

graceful

*Recognizing adverbs; forming adverbs with **-ly***

Making a Fold-Up Book

 Read and follow these directions to make a little book.

1. First tear this page out of the book and turn it over.

2. Next, fold the page along the line of ✶✶✶✶✶✶✶. Make sure the line is on the outside.

3. Next, fold the page along the line of •••••. Be sure the book title is on the outside.

4. Write your name on the line on the title page.

Where Do They Live?

This book belongs to:

_____

Where does the honeybee live?

Where does the red ant live?

The ant lives in a sandy ant hill.

Where does this grey spider live?

The spider lives in a silky web.

Telling About a Toy

Choose one of your favorite toys. Write its name in the square. Think about how the toy looks, sounds, smells, or feels. In each circle, write one detail about the toy. Be sure to use some adjectives.

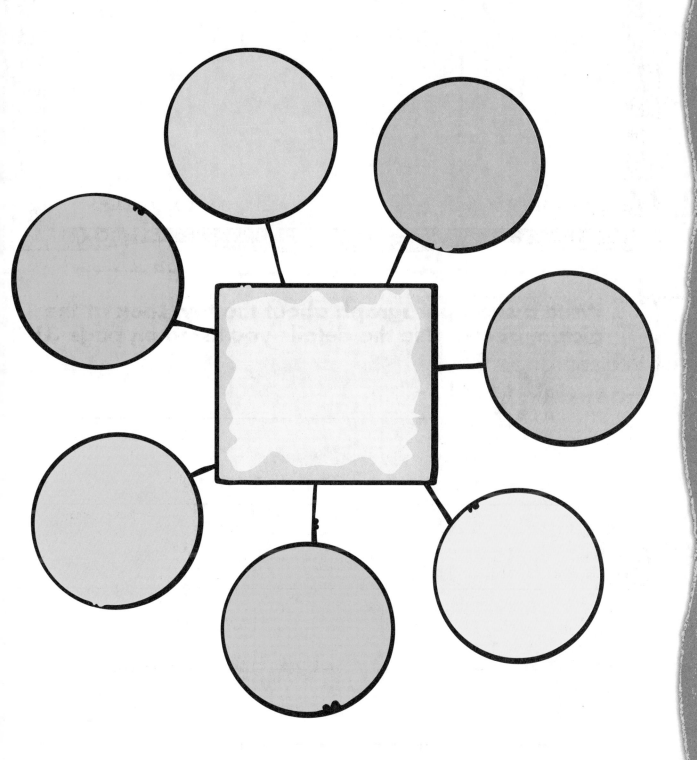

Using a graphic organizer to plan a description

Writing About a Toy

 You wrote details about a favorite toy on page 317. Now draw a picture of the toy.

 Write a short paragraph about the toy. Look at the picture above. Use the details you listed on page 317.

My

Writing a description

Month 11 Checklist

Hands-on activities to help your child in school!

GRAMMAR & PUNCTUATION

Contractions: pages 321-322
Possessive Nouns: pages 323-324
Comparative and Superlative Adjectives: pages 325-326

Help your child master this month's grammar skills with these activities:

❑ Complete the worksheets.
❑ Provide a large sheet of shelf paper and have your child practice writing contractions that are used very often, such as *can't, don't, won't, I'll, we'll, I'm, we're,* and others that are introduced in this month's grammar worksheets.
❑ During drives in business neighborhoods, have your child look for signs that use apostrophes—for example, "Lila's Diner" or "Mike's Garage."

READING

Reading Comprehension: page 347
Cause and Effect: pages 327-328
Inferences and Conclusions: pages 329-330, 335-336
Main Idea: pages 343-344

Use any of the reading activities for this month or from previous months.

❑ Complete the worksheets.
❑ Ask your child to recall a story you have read to him or her. Help your child to understand cause and effect by focusing on a single event and asking, "Why did this event happen?" or "What happened because of this event?"
❑ Give your child practice in inferential thinking. Point out pictures, such as photographs in the news, and ask your child to discuss what events probably came before that scene and what might logically happen next.

SCHOOL BUS

VOCABULARY & WORD STUDY

Compound Words: pages 331-332
Word Parts (Root Words, Prefixes, and Suffixes): pages 337-342

Both compound words and words involving prefixes and suffixes are built from smaller words. Help your child become more aware of word parts with these activities:

❏ Complete the worksheets.
❏ Before reading a page of a story to your child, have him or her scan the page for compound words. Let your child attempt to read the compound word(s) independently and figure out the meaning. Read the page. Then discuss whether your child's definition of each word was accurate.
❏ Post a sheet on the refrigerator door with one of the prefixes or suffixes introduced in this month's worksheets. Ask every member of the family to record words they use or think of that include that word part. At the end of the day, help your child read the words recorded. Repeat the activity another day with a different word part.

COMPOSITION

Adding Details to Sentences: pages 333
Writing a Book Report: pages 348-350

This month's worksheets will help your child recognize the importance of details in writing and introduce the skill of writing a book report.

❏ Complete the worksheets.
❏ Read to your child one or more of these Dr. Seuss books that develop an appreciation for adding details to descriptions: And to Think That I Saw It on Mulberry Street, The 500 Hats of Bartholomew Cubbins, and Scrambled Eggs Super!
❏ After your child has learned to write a book report, have him or her set aside a folder for storing reports of favorite books. This folder will be interesting to both you and your child in years to come.

HANDWRITING

Writing Book Titles: pages 345-346

The handwriting worksheets for this month introduce the rules for writing a book title—minformati needed for writing a book report.

❏ Complete the worksheets.
❏ Have your child write, on separate slips of paper, the titles of at least four books he or she has read recently. Put the papers into a container and shake them. Then draw out one slip, read the title, and have your child tell you what the book was about.

Aren't Contractions Great?

To make a **contraction**, you put two words together. You leave out one or more letters and put in this mark **'** instead. This mark **'** is called an **apostrophe**.

apostrophe

does not = does + no̷t = **doesn't**

He **doesn't** like vegetables.

 Draw a line to match each pair of words with its **contraction**.

did not

could not

is not

are not

can not

do not

 isn't

 can't

 didn't

 aren't

 don't

 couldn't

*Understanding contractions with **not***

We're Using Contractions

A **contraction** is two words put together. One or more letters are left out. In their place is this mark ' called an **apostrophe**.

apostrophe

she will = she + will = **she'll**

She'll eat vegetables anytime!

 Draw a line to match each pair of words with its **contraction**.

he will

we'd

I am

he'll

you are

I'm

we would

she's

she is

it's

it is

you're

Who Owns This?

To show that someone owns a thing, add an **apostrophe** and an **s** to the person's name.

Tracy's hat

Tracy

 To show who owns each thing below, rewrite each person's name, adding an **apostrophe** and an **s** at the end.

Jon's dog
Jon

_____ cat
Amy

_____ bike
Mom

_____ chair
Dad

Understanding possessive nouns

Working with Nouns

To show a person or thing owns something is called showing **possession**. Here is how to make nouns show **possession**.

If the noun names just one, add an **apostrophe** and an **s**.
If the noun names more than one, just add an **apostrophe**.

<u>One</u>
one dog's tail

<u>More Than One</u>
two dogs' tails

 Circle the noun that shows **possession** correctly.

Did I hear one ⬚ **coach's** / **coaches'** ⬚ whistle?

Two ⬚ **dancer's** / **dancers'** ⬚ outfits are pink.

Look at that ⬚ **boy's** / **boys'** ⬚ costume!

Both ⬚ **player's** / **players'** ⬚ caps blew away.

That one is my ⬚ **teacher's** / **teachers'** ⬚ desk.

Understanding how to form singular and plural possessive nouns

Smart and Smarter

We can use adjectives to compare things. Adding **er** to the end of many adjectives makes them compare *two* things.

That cat is **soft**.
This cat is **softer**.

 Each pair of sentences below compares two things. Read the adjective in the first sentence, then rewrite it in the second sentence, adding **er** at the end.

Yesterday was **cold**. Today is even _colder_.

That man is **strong**. This man is _____.

That soup is **warm**. This soup is _____.

That snake is **long**. This snake is _____.

That swing is **high**. This swing is _____.

Introduction to the comparative form of adjectives

Smart, Smarter, Smartest

We can use adjectives to compare things. Adding **est** to the end of many adjectives makes them compare *three or more* things.

tall **taller**  **tallest**

 Rewrite each adjective shown in red, adding **est** at the end to compare all three things.

strong   **stronger**   *strongest*

small   **smaller**   _____

young   **younger**   _____

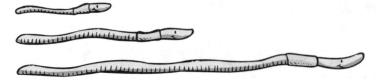

long   **longer**   _____

Introduction to the superlative form of adjectives

Cause and Effect

A cause is the reason why something happens.
An effect is what happens.

Cause

Effect

Because Paul overslept, **he was late for school.**

 Circle the best way to end each sentence.

 **Because Bill runs fast,** *(he won the race.)*

he is a good singer.

Because snow fell, **the sun came out.**

Robin went sledding.

Because it was raining, **Lila is a good friend.**

Lila wore a raincoat.

Because the king is kind, **many people like him.**

he likes ice cream.

A Big Surprise

 Look for causes and effects as you read this story. Then answer the questions below.

Annie was sad. It was her birthday. But none of her friends had wished her a happy birthday all day.

When she came home, she had a big surprise! All her friends were there. "Happy birthday, Annie!" they shouted. Annie felt happy then. Her friends wished her a happy birthday after all.

 Write the answers to these questions.

1. Why was Annie sad?

_____

_____

2. How did the surprise party make Annie feel?

_____

_____

Identifying cause and effect

Using Picture Clues

Sometimes you know something without being told.
You use clues to make guesses.

 Use the picture clues to guess what is happening.
Circle the guess that fits the clues.

This boy just won a race.

This boy just lost a race.

The show is about to begin.

The show is done.

It is very quiet.

The girl hears loud noises.

Sam just ate a jelly sandwich.

Sam has not eaten all day.

Making inferences using visual clues

Using Clues

When you read, you use written clues in the story to figure out what is happening. You use these clues to guess more about what the story means.

Clue

Ann saw her friend. She smiled and waved.

Guess about what it means

Ann is happy to see her friend.

 Read each short story, then circle the guess you think makes the most sense.

Bob was playing outside. Over and over, he asked a friend what time it was. When it was almost 5:00, Bob ran home. As soon as he got inside, he turned on the TV.

You can guess that:

Bob likes the TV show that comes on at 5:00.   **OR**   **Bob eats dinner at 5:00.**

Kim and her dad are fishing. Kim's line is on one side of the boat. Her dad's is on the other side. Kim feels a tug on her line.

You can guess that:

Kim's dad is playing a trick on her.   **OR**   **Kim has caught a fish.**

Reading for inferences

Building Compound Words

A compound word is made of two smaller words.

 +  =

dog + **house** = **doghouse**

 Write a word from the box to finish each compound word below, then write the compound word.

| boat | brush | fire | sand | scare |

sail + _____ = _____

camp + _____ = _____

_____ + **box** = _____

_____ + **crow** = _____

tooth + _____ = _____

Compound Word Coloring

Color the shapes according to the color key to find the hidden picture.

a compound word =

not a compound word =

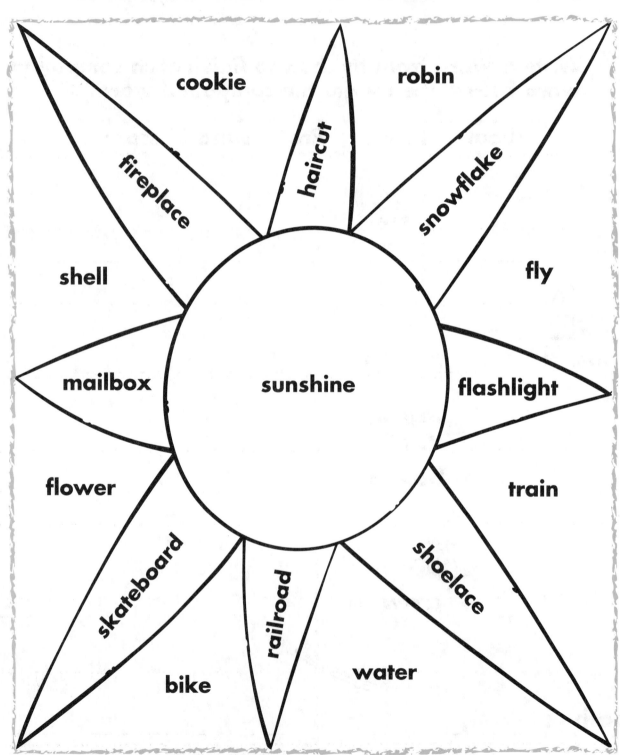

cookie

robin

haircut

fireplace

snowflake

shell

fly

mailbox

sunshine

flashlight

flower

train

skateboard

shoelace

railroad

bike

water

Recognizing compound words

Building Silly Sentences

✂️ Cut out the cards. Each card has a number from 1 to 5. Separate the cards into piles by number. Choose one card from each pile and place them on a table in number order. Read the silly sentence you built! You can do this over and over.

The monster ¹	marched ³	slowly ⁴
The bear ¹	climbed ³	quickly ⁴
The snake ¹	slid ³	quietly ⁴
The cook ¹	looked ³	carefully ⁴

with three eyes ²	to the spaceship. ⁵
with black fur ²	up the tree. ⁵
with shiny scales ²	through the grass. ⁵
with a tall hat ²	into the oven. ⁵

Adding details to sentences

Using Your Head

To solve puzzles, look for clues. Put the clues together with what you already know.

 Look for clues in each picture. Circle the sentence that tells what most likely happened between the two pictures in each row.

The girl threw the ball at the window.

The girl batted the ball through the window.

Someone in the house broke the window.

The sun came out.

It got colder.

Someone pushed the snowman over.

The boy sawed the branch off.

Lightning struck the tree.

The branch broke off.

Drawing conclusions

Putting 2 and 2 Together

A **conclusion** is the answer you come up with after you put together things you know are usually true with things you have guessed.

Spot was in the yard for a while. He is all muddy now. Spot often likes to dig. The garden has been torn up.

Conclusion: Spot wrecked the garden.

 Read about each event and circle the **conclusion** that makes the most sense.

An hour ago, Irene said she was hungry. She went into the kitchen. You know that an apple had been on the counter. The apple is gone now.

A. Irene ate the apple.
B. Irene drank a glass of milk.
C. Irene threw the apple away.

It is the day before your birthday. Your mom tells you to close your eyes. You hear her pull something across the floor. You hear the closet door open and close.

A. Mom hung her coat in the closet.
B. Mom hid a gift for you in the closet.
C. Mom hid cake and ice cream in the closet.

Drawing conclusions

Building from the Roots!

A **root word** is a whole word that can have word parts added to it. A **prefix** is the word part added to the beginning of a **root word**. The **prefix** un means "not."

prefix		root word		
un	+	tied	=	**untied**

Untied means "not tied."

Add **un** to the beginning of each **root word** below to make a new word. Circle the meaning of the new word.

un̲ happy   **not happy**   **happy**

____ lucky   **lucky**   **not lucky**

____ ripe   **ripe**   **not ripe**

____ safe   **not safe**   **safe**

____ opened   **opened**   **not opened**

Building Words: The Prefix re

Prefixes are word parts added to the beginning of **root words**. The **prefix re** means "again."

prefix		root word		
re	+	build	=	**rebuild**

Rebuild means "build again."

 Add **re** to the beginning of each **root word** below to make a new word. Circle the meaning of the new word.

_____ read   **read   read again**

_____ try   **try   try again**

_____ play   **play again   play**

_____ heat   **heat   heat again**

_____ write   **write again   write**

338

Understanding root words and word parts: prefixes

Building Words: The Suffix ful

A **suffix** is a word part added to the end of a **root word**.
The **suffix ful** means "full of."

root word   suffix

peace   **+**   **ful**   **=**   **peaceful**

Peaceful means "full of peace."

 Draw a line to match each word with its meaning.

graceful   **full of tears**

useful   **full of grace**

tearful   **full of play**

playful   **full of use**

 Rewrite each **root word** in bold and add the **suffix ful** at the end.

I feel full of **joy**. I feel _____ .

Take good **care** of that. Be _____ .

Building Words: The Suffix less

Suffixes are word parts added to the ends of **root words.**
The **suffix less** means "without."

root word   suffix

hair   **+**   less   **=**   **hairless**

Hairless means "without hair."

 Underline the **suffix** in each of these words.

painless   **hopeless**   **colorless**   **nameless**

 Write one of the words above to match each meaning below.

_____   _____
without hope   **without a name**

_____   _____
without pain   **without color**

 Write a word with the **suffix less** to complete the sentence.

The cat is without a home.

It is _____.

Building Words: The Suffix ly

Suffixes are word parts added to the ends of **root words**. The **suffix ly** means "in this way."

VOCABULARY & WORD STUDY

root word   suffix

brave + **ly** = **bravely**

Bravely means "in a brave way."

 Underline the **suffix** in each of these words.

surely   **roughly**   **brightly**   **sadly**

 Write one of the words above to match each meaning below.

_____
in a bright way

_____
in a sure way

_____
in a rough way

_____
in a sad way

 Write a word with the **suffix ly** to complete the sentence.

The snail moves in a slow way.

It moves _____ .

Reviewing Word Parts

 Underline the **prefix** in each word below. Draw a line between each word and its meaning.

rewrite	not sure
redraw	write again
unafraid	draw again
unsure	not afraid

 Underline the **suffix** in each word in the box. Then write a word from the box to complete each sentence.

peaceful	quickly	wordless	neatly	hopeful

Do your work in a neat way. Do it _____.

The song has no words. It is _____.

I am full of hope. I am _____.

This place is full of peace. It is _____.

The little bird moves in a quick way.

It moves _____.

Looking for the Main Idea

The main idea of a paragraph is its most important idea.

 **Read each paragraph, then circle its main idea.**

The city is a noisy place. Cars honk their horns. Brakes squeal. Sirens scream. People call to each other. Music from radios fills the air.

There are lots of people in the city.

The city is noisy.

Mom works hard in her garden. She plants flowers in rows. She pulls weeds. She trims the bushes and sweeps the paths. All her work makes the garden pretty.

Weeds should always be pulled.

Mom works hard to make her garden pretty.

Identifying the main idea

Where's the Main Idea?

The main idea of a paragraph is its most important idea.

 **Read each paragraph, then fill in the ⬭ next to its main idea.**

My family took a nice trip. We drove a long way. We stayed at a fancy motel. We got to Grandma's house the next day. Grandma was glad to see us. I hope we go on a trip again.

○ **Trips can be fun.**
○ **Grandma went on a trip.**
○ **Trips are too much work.**

Fall is the best time of the year. In fall, the leaves are pretty. They turn red and yellow. Soon the leaves fall down. I rake them into piles. Then I jump into the piles. I like fall.

○ **Leaves are pretty.**
○ **Fall is a good time of year.**
○ **Fall is a long time away.**

Identifying the main idea

One Boy's Favorites

 Kevin made a list of his favorite books. Read the list. See how Kevin underlined all the words. Circle each capital letter.

My Favorite Books
Oogle and Moogle
How to Talk to a Martian
A Day in the Life of a Slime Monster

 Where are capital letters used in book titles? Fill in the ○ next to each correct answer.

○ **every word in the title**

○ **first word in the title**

○ **last word in the title**

○ **little words like** *of,* *in,* **and** *the* **when they are** *not* **first or last**

○ **names of people and things**

○ **verbs**

○ **other important words, even when they are not first or last**

Good Titles

Fill in the ○ next to each title that is correctly written.

○ **He is Friends with a Chicken**

○ **he Is Friends With a chicken**

○ **Kids' Favorite Mushroom Recipes**

○ **Kids' favorite Mushroom recipes**

○ **stamp collectors Like Spinach!**

○ **Stamp Collectors Like Spinach!**

Write the titles of your two favorite books.
Use capital letters and underlining.

1. _____

2. _____

Understanding the mechanics of writing book titles

Telling About a Book

 Read Kevin's book report.

I like the book <u>Oogle and Moogle</u>. It was written by Frank Persico.

The book is about two ducks, Oogle and Moogle, who want to move from Florida to Iceland. It is a long way to fly, but an airplane pilot named Joe helps them out. After they get to Iceland, they have to decide if they want to stay there or not.

<u>Oogle and Moogle</u> is a funny book. I really like the part when Oogle tries to fly the plane.

 Draw a line from each question to its answer.

What is the title of the book?

Who wrote the book?

Who is in the book?

What happens in the book?

What special part does Kevin like?

Frank Persico

two ducks want to fly from Florida to Iceland

when Oogle tries to fly the plane

two ducks and an airplane pilot

<u>**Oogle and Moogle**</u>

Telling About a Book

Choose a book you want to write a report about. Fill in the boxes below with facts about that book. You can use these facts when you write your report.

QUESTIONS	FACTS
What is the title of the book?	
Who wrote the book?	
Who is in the book?	
What happens in the book?	
What part do you like best?	

Using a graphic organizer for a book report

Writing a Book Report, Part 1

 Now it's your turn to write a book report! In the box, draw a picture of someone in the book.

 Write the first part of your report. Write sentences that tell these facts:

- **the title of the book**
- **who wrote it**
- **who is in it**

_____

_____

_____

_____

Writing a Book Report, Part 2

 Now finish your book report! In the box, draw a picture of something that happens in the book.

 Write sentences that tell what happens in the book. Also tell what part you like best.

_____

_____

_____

_____

_____

_____

Month 12 Checklist

Hands-on activities to help your child in school!

HANDWRITING

Writing an Invitation: pages 353-354
Addressing an Envelope: pages 355-356

Despite the use of e-mail and the telephone, writing social notes such as invitations and thank-you notes is still an important social skill. Give your child practice in writing notes and addressing envelopes with these activities:

❑ Complete the worksheets.
❑ When you plan a party either for your child's friends or for your family, have your child write all the invitations and, if possible, the envelopes. If you like, have your child write just one invitation, leaving the recipient's name blank, and make sure it is error-free. Then make photocopies and help your child fill in the names of the guests.

READING

Reading Comprehension: pages 369-370
Predicting Outcomes: pages 357-358
Making Inferences: pages 359-360
Elements of a Story: pages 371, 373, 375

This month's worksheets about elements of a story prepare your child for writing an original story. They focus on the most important elements of any story: who is in the story, where and when it happens, and what happens. Help your child develop this month's reading skills with these activities:

❑ Complete the worksheets.
❑ Continue strengthening inferential skills with the activity suggested in the Month 11 Checklist.
❑ When talking about the stories you read with your child, or movies and TV shows you watch together, reinforce the concept of story elements by asking your child questions such as these: Who is the story about? Where does the story take place? When does it happen? What are some of the events that happen? Also invite your child to state if he or she liked the story and to explain why or why not.

COMPOSITION

Combining Sentences: pages 361-366
Writing a Story: pages 372, 374, 376-382

This month's composition worksheets lead your child through the entire process of writing an original story: choosing characters, deciding on a setting, and developing a plot. Pages 377 and 378 guide your child in putting all the parts together to create his or her own storybook. Your child can use the worksheets to develop all three elements of the story to be put into the storybook. The final pages for this month offer some story starter pictures and accompanying worksheets to help inspire creative thinking.

❑ Complete the worksheets.

❑ As your child develops a story, or future stories, encourage him or her to work out the plot with puppets or dolls taking the parts of characters. If your child is agreeable, help by operating one or more of the puppet characters and volunteering words or ideas.

VOCABULARY & WORD STUDY

Vocabulary Review: pages 367-368

Activities for this month review synonyms, antonyms, homonyms, and compound words.

❑ Complete the worksheets.

❑ State a pair of words, such as *pretty/beautiful* or *pretty/ugly*, and have your child decide which group the word pair belongs in: synonyms or antonyms.

Please Come!

 Read this invitation. Underline every capital letter in the invitation.

August 4, 2003

Dear Steve,

    Can you come to a picnic next Saturday, August 9? We'll swim, play ball, and eat hot dogs and ice cream. Mom will drive us to the park at noon and bring us back about four o'clock. I hope you can come. Please let me know by Wednesday.

Your pal,
Manny

 Some words always begin with capital letters. Match each word below with the right word group.

August	**First word of sentence**
Please	**First word of letter part**
Mom	**Name of person**
Wednesday	**Name of day**
Your	**Name of month**

Writing an invitation (capitalization)

Writing an Invitation

Imagine you could invite anyone to lunch. Whom would you invite?

Fill in this invitation. Write these things:
Line 1: today's date
Line 2: the name of the person you are inviting
Lines 3-7: the day, time, and place of your lunch
Line 8: your own name

(1) _____ , **200** _____

(2) **Dear** _____ ,

(3) _____

(4) _____

(5) _____

(6) _____

(7) _____

Your friend,

(8) _____

Going Somewhere

 Read this envelope. Then answer the questions below.

name → Mary Music
house number → 987 Harmony Lane ← street
city → Song Town, Ohio 42864
state
zip code or post code

 Answer these questions. Remember to use capital letters correctly.

1. To what zip code is it going? _____

2. To what town? _____

3. To what state? _____

4. To what street? _____

5. To what person? _____

Addressing an Envelope

 Write an address on this envelope using this information:

Name—Peter Piper
House number—123
Street—Paradise Pass

City—Pickles
State—Pennsylvania
Zip code—15234

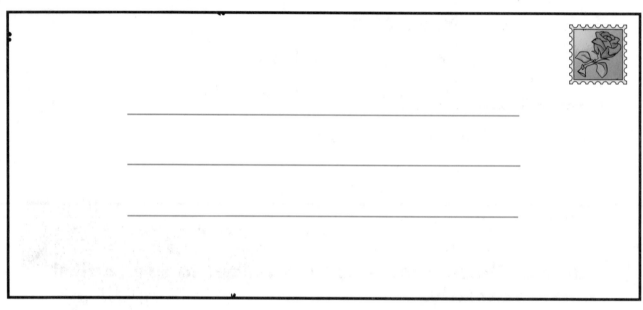

 Write your own address on this envelope.

What Will They Do?

 Read each story beginning, then circle the sentence ending that makes the most sense.

Brendan woke up excited and happy. The sun was shining. It was a perfect day for a trip to the beach. After a few seconds, Brendan

jumped out of bed.

rolled over and went back to sleep.

Maggie knew a storm was coming. The sky was gray. A strong wind began to blow. Thunder rolled. Maggie decided to

go outside and play.

stay inside with her family.

Dee was ready for the dance show. She had done her steps over and over. Before the show, she felt sure of herself. She smiled as she came onto the stage. Then Dee

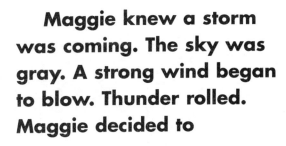

forgot all the dance steps.

did the dance well.

Predicting outcomes

What Will Happen Next?

 Read this part of a story. Think about what might happen next.

The puppy knew the rules. He should not sit on the new chair. Still, one day he was home alone and felt so tired! He looked at the new chair. It seemed like a good place for a nap.

 Draw a picture of what happens next.

 Write about what happens next.

_____

_____

_____

Predicting outcomes

A Picture Detective

 Use the picture clues to guess what is happening. Circle the guess that fits the clues.

This girl likes carrots.

This girl does not like carrots.

Today is windy.

There is no wind today.

The bag is heavy.

The bag is light.

The team just lost the game.

The team just won the game.

Making inferences using visual clues

Reading for Clues

The exact words you read may not give you all the facts. Sometimes you need to look for clues to guess what is happening.

 Read each paragraph, looking for clues, then fill in the ◯ next to the sentence that tells what is happening.

People on a train are putting on their coats and hats. They are picking up what belongs to them. They are standing up and looking out the windows.

From these clues you can guess that:

◯ **The train is about to stop.**

◯ **The train is about to begin its trip.**

On the table at a party are two bowls of food. The first bowl is almost empty. The second bowl is still full.

From these clues you can guess that:

◯ **The guests like the food in the first bowl better.**

◯ **The guests like the food in the second bowl better.**

Reading for inferences

The Magic of And

Use the word and to change two sentences into one sentence.

Frogs **hopped.** Toads **hopped.**
Frogs **and** toads **hopped.**

 Change two sentences into one. Write a new sentence using and between the two nouns shown in red.

Flies **buzzed.** Bees **buzzed.**

_____ **buzzed.**

Dogs **ran.** Cats **ran.**

_____ **ran.**

Girls **played soccer.** Boys **played soccer.**

_____ **played soccer.**

Rain **ruined the picnic. Wind ruined the picnic.**

_____ **ruined the picnic.**

Put Yourself Last

Use and to change two sentences into one sentence. If you are writing a sentence using the pronoun I, always put it second.

She swam. I swam.
She **and** I swam.

 Change two sentences into one. Write a new sentence using and between the two pronouns shown in red.

He read the book. I read the book.

_____ read the book.

She wore boots. I wore boots.

_____ wore boots.

You like soccer. I like soccer.

_____ like soccer.

She lives on Oak Road. I live on Oak Road.

_____ live on Oak Road.

Combining sentences by making compound subjects with pronouns

Picnic Time

Use the word and to change two sentences into one sentence.

The park has swings.
The park has picnic tables.

The park has swings **and** picnic tables.

 Change two sentences into one. Write a new sentence using and between the two nouns shown in red.

We ate fruit. We ate burgers.

We ate _____ .

I like pop. I like juice.

I like _____ .

We played tag. We played catch.

We played _____ .

We saw geese. We saw ducks.

We saw _____ .

Combining sentences by making compound objects with nouns

Me Last!

Use and to change two sentences into one sentence. If you are writing a sentence using the pronoun me, always put it second.

Mary walked with Jan.
Mary walked with me.

Mary walked with Jan **and** me.

 **Read each pair of sentences. A new sentence that combines them has been started. Draw a line to the correct way to end the sentence.**

Dad read a story to Jason.
Dad read a story to me.

Dad read a story to   Jason and me.
me and Jason.

Sherri visited Luis.
Sherri visited me.

Sherri visited   me and Luis.
Luis and me.

Laura waved to me.
Laura waved to you.

Laura waved to   me and you.
you and me.

Combining sentences by making compound objects with pronouns

Combining Sentences

You can make one sentence from two sentences.
Use **and** to join the verbs.

Derek ran.
Derek swam.

Derek ran **and** swam.

 Change two sentences into one. Write a new sentence
using **and** between the two verbs shown in red.

Mary coughs. Mary sneezes.

Mary _____.

 My dog barks. My dog begs.

My dog _____.

The glass fell. The glass broke.

The glass _____.

The giant shouts. The giant roars.

The giant _____.

Combining sentences by making compound verbs

Using Or and But

Here are two other ways to make one sentence from two sentences.

Use the word **or**.

Sally may paint.
Sally may read.
Sally may paint **or** read.

Use the word **but**.

The movie was good.
The movie was long.
The movie was good **but** long.

 Write one sentence that combines two sentences.
Use **or** or **but**.

I could eat fruit.
I could eat crackers.

_____

Today is sunny.
Today is cold.

_____

The soup is tasty.
The soup is too hot.

_____

Word Balloons

Antonyms are words with opposite meanings, such as **in** and **out**. Synonyms are words with the same or nearly the same meaning, such as **little** and **small**.

 Each balloon has either two antonyms or two synonyms.
Color the balloons with antonyms .
Color the balloons with synonyms .

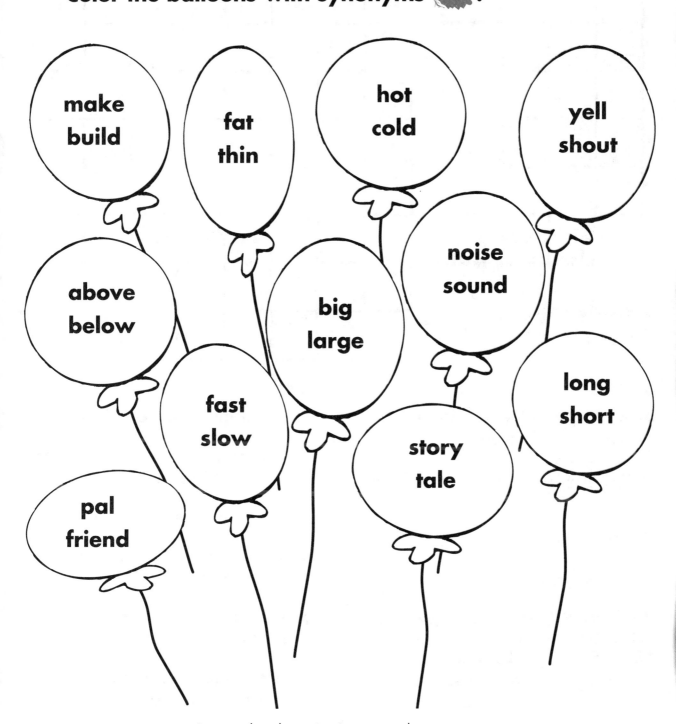

make
build

fat
thin

hot
cold

yell
shout

above
below

noise
sound

big
large

long
short

fast
slow

story
tale

pal
friend

Distinguishing between antonyms and synonyms

Word Fun

 Use the clues to solve this crossword puzzle.

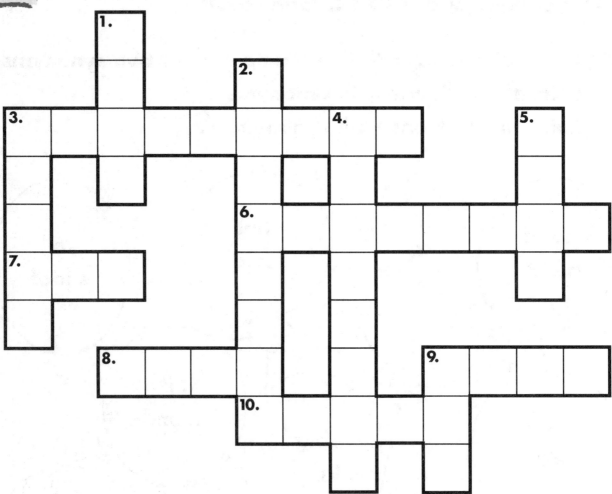

ACROSS

3. A compound word for a berry that is blue

6. A compound word for a boat with a sail

7. The opposite of **on**

8. The opposite of **empty**

9. A word that sounds like **cent**

10. A synonym for **go**
It rhymes with **weave.**

DOWN

1. The number before five

2. A compound word for a shell you find in the sea

3. The opposite of **above**

4. A compound word for a road made of rails

5. A synonym for **take**
It rhymes with cab.

9. A synonym for **look**
It sounds like **sea.**

368 _____ *Reviewing synonyms, antonyms, homonyms, and compound words* _____

The Balloon Party

Slowly the air came out of the balloons. The children floated back to the ground. David laughed and clapped. What a great surprise! His friends agreed that was the most fun they ever had at a party.

David said, "This is my best birthday ever!"

David had a birthday party. He gave each of his friends a balloon. The balloons were very big! The children took them outside.

The wind blew. It blew hard! It was so strong it pulled the balloons up...up...up! The children held tight to their balloons.

The wind grew stronger! It pulled David up...up...up! He was so surprised! It pulled his friends up! They all began to laugh! They were floating!

Just then, some birds flew by. They pecked at the balloons. Peck, peck, peck. They pecked tiny holes in the balloons.

Who?

Usually, a story tells what happens to a person or an animal, or several people or animals.

 Read the story "The Balloon Party." Pay attention to the people and animals in the story. Circle all the correct answers to each question.

1. Who is in the story?

David	David's mother	David's father
David's dog	birds	David's friends

2. Who is the most important person in the story?

David   David's mother   David's best friend

3. Which of these words tell about David?

grown-up	young	sleepy
happy	sad	surprised
a girl	a crow	a boy

Recognizing the characters of a story

The Hero of Your Story

 **Read this chart.
It tells about David in "The Balloon Party."**

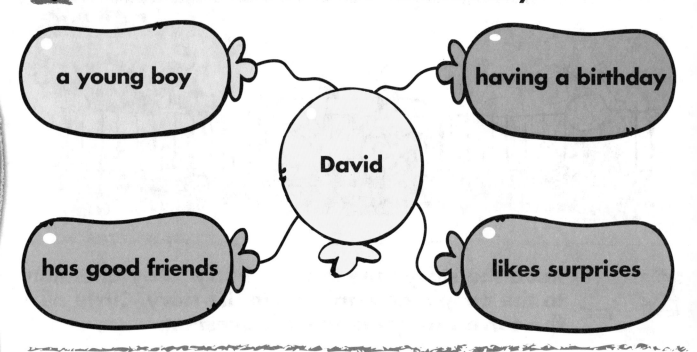

a young boy

having a birthday

David

has good friends

likes surprises

 Start your own story. First choose a person or animal to write about. Then fill in the chart to tell more about the person or animal.

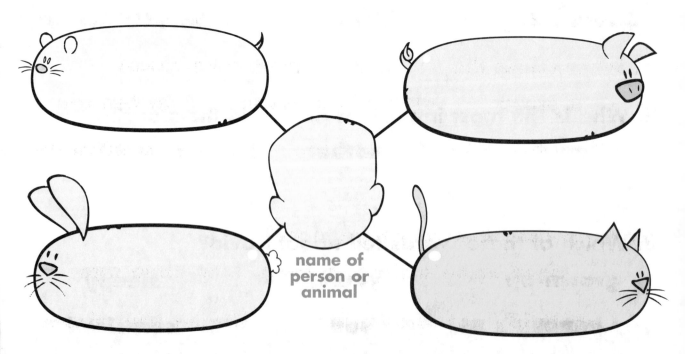

name of person or animal

If you need help thinking of a story, turn to pages 379 and 380 for ideas.

Using a graphic organizer for planning a story's character

Where and When?

Often, a story tells what happens in or around one place. Often, the action happens at one time or close to one time.

 Read the story "The Balloon Party." Pay attention to the people and animals in the story. Circle all the correct answers to each question.

1. Where does the action in the story take place?

    in a store   at David's house   in the air

    on the moon   outside   in a kitchen

2. When does the story take place?

    once upon a time, a long, long time ago

  probably not long ago   during the winter

      during a birthday party

Recognizing the setting of a story

Choosing Where and When

You can choose any time or place for a story! The time can be past, present, or future. The place can be anywhere. It can even be a made-up place.

 Look at these pictures. They show where and when the action in "The Balloon Party" happens.

 **Draw where your story takes place. Circle the word below that tells when it happens.**

Place

Time: past   present   future

Using a graphic organizer (sketch) to plan a story's setting

What's Happening?

In most stories, what happens is the most important part. It can make us laugh and it can make us think.

 Number what happens in "The Balloon Party" in correct order from 1–4.

_____ **The children float down to the ground.**

_____ **The wind pulls the balloons and the children into the air.**

_____ **David gives each of his friends a balloon.**

_____ **Birds peck tiny holes in the balloons.**

You Can Make It Happen!

When you write a story, you can make anything happen! Think about the important events in the story you want to write. Make sure that one action leads to the next.

 Fill in this chart. In each box, write a short sentence about the important events in your story. Put the events in order.

1

2

3

4

Graphic organizer for planning plot/events of original story

Get Ready to Write!

Before you write your story, pull all your ideas together.

  Fill in this chart. Read page 378 before you write the whole story.

Title _____

Who is in the story? _____

_____

Where and when does it take place? _____

_____

What happens in the story? _____

_____

_____

_____

_____

_____

Using a graphic organizer for writing an original story

Sharing Your Story

Your chart on page 377 makes your story clear to you. Follow these steps to share it with others.

1. Write your story on your own paper. Use your best handwriting.

2. Draw pictures for your story on more paper. Color them.

3. Use another piece of paper to make a front cover. Write the title on the cover. If you like, draw a picture, too.

4. Use another piece of paper to make a back cover. Lay the story and the pictures on top of it.

5. Lay the front cover on top of everything. Staple the pages together.

6. Let others read your story.

Story Starters

 You can write your own story. These pictures will help to give you ideas.

Picture prompts for writing an original story

More Story Starters

 Here are more ideas for stories.

Picture prompts for writing an original story

Story Starters Worksheet

 Choose one of the pictures from page 379 or 380. Use this worksheet to help you plan a story about it.

1. If you wrote a story about this picture, what title would you give the story?

_____

2. What name would you give the most important person or animal in the story?

_____

3. Write four words that tell about this person or animal.

_____   _____

_____   _____

4. Where would your story take place? If there would be more than one place, write about each one.

_____

_____

_____

_____

Story Starters Worksheet (cont'd)

5. When would the events in your story happen?

_____

_____

6. Write the four most important events that would happen in your story. Write them in order, from 1–4.

1. _____

2. _____

3. _____

4. _____

Draw another picture for your story.

Story starter worksheet

Index